CAREERS AND OPPORTUNITIES
IN CHEMISTRY

By Philip Pollack

CAREERS AND OPPORTUNITIES IN SCIENCE

YOUR CAREER IN PHYSICS

CAREERS AND OPPORTUNITIES IN ENGINEERING

CAREERS AND OPPORTUNITIES IN CHEMISTRY

CAREERS

AND OPPORTUNITIES

IN CHEMISTRY

A Survey of All Fields

BY PHILIP POLLACK

With an Introduction by GEORGE M. MURPHY
Professor of Chemistry and Head of the All-University Department of Chemistry, New York University

ILLUSTRATED

E. P. DUTTON & CO., INC., NEW YORK

First Printing, March, 1960
Second Printing, April, 1961
Third Printing, April, 1962
Fourth Printing, April, 1966

To DR. LINUS C. PAULING
*For his achievements as a scientist
and his integrity as a man*

Acknowledgments

FOR PERTINENT SUGGESTIONS AND CRITICISMS IN THE PREPARA-
tion of the manuscript, the author wishes to acknowledge
his especial indebtedness to Dr. Robert P. Frankenthal,
chemist, of the Applied Research Laboratory, United States
Steel Corporation, whose devotion to science is matched
only by his unselfish desire to help educate others; to Karl
Haber, chemist and director of the Pilot Plant, Research
Division, S. B. Penick Company, Inc.; to Miss Hoylande D.
Young, chemist and director of the Technical Information
Service of the Argonne National Laboratory; to the editors
of *Chemical and Engineering News;* and to his wife, Flora,
who slaved away at the typewriter with incredible devo-
tion, speed, and efficiency.

Introduction

by GEORGE M. MURPHY, *Professor of Chemistry and Head of the All-University Department of Chemistry, New York University*

MOST OF US, SOMETIME IN OUR CHILDHOOD, PLANNED TO BE explorers, aviators, soldiers, or something of that sort, when we grew up. The child of today frequently thinks of space travel or has even more exciting ideas. Eventually, and perhaps reluctantly, we all recognize that there may be advantages in a less glamorous profession offering more security and intellectual challenge. The next conclusion is usually much more difficult to reach. Fortunate, indeed, are the young men and women who know what they want to do, who acquire the appropriate education for that chosen career, and who are happy in it. A much greater number of youths find themselves in the less fortunate position of not knowing what they want to make of their lives, or of learning, too late, that they are tragically unsuited for the professions in which they have been trained.

Teachers in our schools and colleges are well aware of these difficulties, and they spend considerable time in career guidance and counselling. Too often, and apparently quite frequently in the natural sciences, the resulting advice to students may be either unduly optimistic or unduly pessimistic. It is easy, for example, to describe a chemist as someone working in a laboratory filled with fascinating apparatus, and daily producing wonderful inventions and discoveries of profound scientific importance. At the other extreme, he may be depicted as a misunderstood genius whose brilliant achievements are only appreciated after his untimely death. The truth, of course, is quite different from either of these common misconceptions.

We should be grateful, therefore, to the author of this book, who tells us what a chemist is, how one learns to be a chemist, and what the chemist does in his professional life. Starting with a remarkably concise history of the subject, beginning with the alchemists, we are quickly transported to our present technological age, which would be impossible without the chemist. The book continues with a detailed survey of many specialized fields of chemistry, describing in each case the opportunities and special skills involved. All of this information is presented in a highly readable and absorbing fashion. It is enlivened by true accounts of problems attacked and solved by chemists. The facts of the profession, including typical salaries and future demands for chemists, are carefully documented.

The title of the book is self-explanatory and suggests the audience to which it is addressed. Let us consider, however, some types of individuals to whom it may be of help. First of all, think of those talented boys and girls who are fascinated by chemistry sets in early childhood, with enthusiasm and good grades continuing in their pre-college years. Their parents might ask such precocious offspring to read this book carefully. It will be useful to them. Next, remember the frustrated space travelers and explorers. They too will certainly find profit in the chapters which follow. Finally, suppose that you are a student, undergraduate or graduate, committed to a career as a chemist, or even a professional chemist engaged in research or industry. In either case you will be interested in this survey of your chosen field.

There are two points in particular that I would like to make:

Sometimes a student will decide, for one reason or another, that he wants to be a petroleum chemist, a food chemist, or an expert in some other of the many specialized branches of the science. With the impatience of youth, he may be bored with studying elementary organic chemistry, quantitative analysis, thermodynamics, or molecular structure. German, calculus, and other non-chemical subjects may seem even more tedious, for they appear to be useless in the career which he has planned for himself. Such conclusions, of course, are completely false. If one wants to be a technician, he should go to a trade school; if one wants to be a chemist, he must learn the fundamental disciplines of the subject. Whatever may be his field of later specialization, he will find that his contributions to it and his distinction in it will depend to a large extent on the breadth and depth of his basic chemical knowledge.

The second comment is, in some respects, the inverse of the first. Many bright chemistry majors, as seniors, have become so excited by what they have learned in college that they find it difficult to choose between organic chemistry, physical chemistry, or other specialties. It will be assumed that the student recognizes, as a graduating senior, that an advanced degree is highly desirable. Let him then postpone his decision about a special field as long as possible. The answer to his problem will come, usually with complete certainty. He may be influenced by a particular teacher whom he admires, by a book that he may read, or by some other, seemingly trivial encounter. Once the decision is made, let him never regret it. There are enough unsolved problems in all branches of chemistry to keep our students busy for many years in the future.

GEORGE M. MURPHY

November 30, 1959

Contents

		PAGE
	Acknowledgments	vi
	Introduction	vii

CHAPTER

1	Chemistry Is Born	3
2	The Chemical Profession Today	15
3	Qualifications and Training	26
4	The Organic Chemist	38
5	The Inorganic Chemist	55
6	The Analytical Chemist	68
7	The Biochemist	77
8	Physical Chemistry and Other Fields of Chemistry	96
9	The Chemical Engineer	107
10	The Chemist as Technical Salesman	117
11	Calling All Women Chemists!	124
	Appendix	134
	Notes and References	139
	Index	143

Photographs

FACING PAGE

An example of teamwork: research chemists thrashing out basic theoretic problems in the process of developing Delrin plastic   20

Research chemist W. G. Guldner with apparatus for measuring the surface area of powdered metals   20

Organic chemist making a study of organic processes by means of radioactive "tracers"   21

Two organic chemists analyze a problem in polymerization   21

Inorganic chemist Lucille Finneran making a test to determine the durability of glass in alkaline solutions   52

Inorganic chemist Ted McKinley testing titanium crystals   53

Using the spectograph to make qualitative and quantitative analyses of materials   53

If you become an analytical chemist, you will probably work in a laboratory similar to this one   84

Biochemist studying the effects of chemicals on blood cells   85

Chemist operating a manipulator in the fabrication of radioactive material   116

Chemical engineer at work in a pilot plant which simulates large-scale production   116

Chemical salesmen serve as important links between the research laboratory and the consumer   117

Women make excellent chemists   117

CAREERS AND OPPORTUNITIES
IN CHEMISTRY

CHAPTER ONE

Chemistry Is Born

MANY PEOPLE HAVE ONLY A VAGUE IDEA OF WHAT A CHEMIST is or the kind of work he does. In some minds the word evokes association words like "druggist" or "pharmacist," for pharmacists in England are called chemists, and many American pharmacists use the same designation. Yet a chemist is not a pharmacist and a pharmacist is not a chemist, in the correct meaning of the term.

Chemistry deals with the chemical composition and properties of matter, both animate and inanimate, and with the reactions and transformations of elements and compounds under different conditions. The scope of chemistry is limitless. It embraces manufacturing, agriculture, medicine, and many other fields.

Look at yourself in the mirror. What you see reflects a few of the countless contributions of the chemist. He discovered or developed the synthetic fibers of which your clothes may be made; the dyes that give them attractive coloring; the cellulose nitrate of the plastic frame of your spectacles; the silicate compounds in the glass, both of the mirror and of the lenses of your spectacles. The telephone rings and you lift up the receiver, unaware of the fact that forty-four different chemicals were used in its manufacture. Virtually anything made by man that you touch, use, operate, drive, eat, or swallow as medicine when you are ill required the services of the chemist at one stage or another—including not only the food you eat but also the pots and pans used in cooking it. All these things involved the application of chemical compounds that had to be discovered, developed, analyzed, tested, and finally mass produced by chemical engineering methods.

Chemistry is an exact science like physics or astronomy. It was born of man's insatiable hunger for knowledge of the laws that govern life and the universe. Its by-product is the chemical industry, which manufactures innumerable industrial, agricultural, and pharmaceutical materials, from plastics, abrasives, and synthetic fibers to acids, alcohols, food flavorings, fungicides and insecticides. If you visited a large chemical plant for the first time, you would probably be overawed at the sight of the Gargantuan red-hot revolving ovens and the tangled nests of crooked pipes and vats. After standing for a while in such a plant, you might well wonder how chemistry began and what it was like in earlier centuries. Let us close our eyes for a moment and imagine that we are back in the Middle Ages. . . .

We find ourselves in an alchemist's laboratory, cluttered with crucibles, stills, and alembics. The alchemist is working a pair of bellows to blow up the flame in the furnace. Muttering secret incantations, he holds a vial containing yellow sulfur and mercury over the fire and then adds silver, pure oil of olives, and molten lead. His object is to discover the *materia prima*, or philosophers' stone, by means of which he could transform base metals like iron and lead into gold, cure human illnesses, and restore vigorous youth to the aged. . . .

Today we smile at such obsessions. Yet the modern chemist owes much to the alchemist. In the course of his experiments with chemicals, the alchemist stumbled on discoveries that paved the way for the development of modern chemistry. Three of the most important acids used today—nitric, hydrochloric, and sulfuric acids—were originally discovered by alchemists, and the same is true of bismuth, antimony, barium sulfide, and many other chemicals.[1] The very retorts, distilling flasks, and cupels (used for assaying) that are today essential tools in the chemist's laboratory were invented by these fanatical seekers of the unattainable.

The earliest development of the arts related to chemistry antedated the appearance of the first alchemist by many centuries. Indeed, chemical arts were practiced in Egypt as far back as from 1100 to 1400 B.C. It is significant that the word "Egypt" in hieroglyphics is *quemi* or *chemi* (meaning "the black land"), from which the word "chemistry" is derived.[2] Metal and glass objects, pottery and dyed materials —these constitute the earliest evidence we have of the use of chemical processes. The ancient Egyptians were skilled in tanning, dyeing, and metalworking; indeed, one of the earliest known pieces of gold jewelry, found in Egypt, dates from as far back as 3400 B.C.

It was not, however, in Egypt but in ancient Greece that chemical theories originated, as recorded in the teachings of the Greek philosophers. Thus, Thales taught that the primordial element, from which all other elements are derived, was water. Empedocles (born about 490 B.C.) believed that all matter consisted of four elements—earth, air, water, and fire—combined in different proportions, according to the nature of the substance. (For example, he taught that bone consisted of one-fourth earth, one-fourth water,

---

[1] See *Notes and References*, beginning on page 139.

and one-half fire.[3]) These four elements, according to Empedocles, were fixed and unchangeable and differed only in their proportions. Aristotle also believed in this theory; but, unlike Empedocles, he taught that the elements could be modified and transformed by agencies that changed their inherent qualities, such as wetness, dryness, coldness, and heat. Aristotle's views had tremendous influence on future generations, and he was often quoted by alchemists in support of their claim that base metals could be transformed into gold.

The chemical arts flourished in the Roman Empire, but, as in engineering and other sciences, the Romans contributed little to theoretic analysis, despite their practical work in engineering. However, they were ingenious in making pigments, dyes, medicines, and inks, and developed a cement that set under water, as well as a method of extracting mercury from cinnabar.[4]

It was by means of translations from the Arabic that alchemy was first introduced into the Latin world. The oldest translation of which we have any record, was dated A.D. 1144. Roger Bacon was only one of the many Schoolmen who performed experiments in an attempt to transmute base metals into gold. Some were drawn to alchemy for metaphysical reasons. Thus, the alchemist Albertus Magnus speculated on the apparent attraction of sulfur for the metals; his analysis, though mystical, suggests the later concept of chemical affinity.

The chemical arts continued to develop through the Middle Ages. Most of our knowledge of this development is derived from medical writings and prescriptions that have come down to us. Salernus, a physician who lived in the twelfth century, was the first to describe a method of distilling alcohol. Theophilus the priest wrote "recipes" (prescriptions) for making glues, dyes, and inks.

The most important chemical figure in the sixteenth century—and one far in advance of his times—was Paracelsus, a Swiss physician and astrologer. He taught that biologic life is a chemical process and that illness should be treated with chemicals—an unusual concept at that time. He was one of the earliest physicians to prescribe inorganic salts instead of the usual herbs for his sick patients, and introduced tincture of opium, which he called laudanum, as a curative drug. Some of the pharmaceuticals prescribed by physicians today are basically the same as those used by Paracelsus, for example, iron and zinc salts. With the contributions of this remarkable man, chemistry began to emerge from the chrysalis of alchemy. "The true use of chemistry," he wrote, "is not to make gold but to prepare medicines." [5]

It was not until the seventeenth century that the first important generalization to explain chemical phenomena was developed—the "phlogiston" theory, first proposed by Johann Joachim Becker and later elaborated by Georg Ernst Stahl. According to this theory, all combustible substances were composed of phlogiston (from the Greek, meaning "to set on fire"). When they burned, this ingredient became visible in the form of flame. It might, however, take other forms, and Stahl explained the rusting of iron and the transformation of heated metal into powder as manifestations of phlogiston. This theory dominated the thinking of chemists for over a century. Though later proved to be fallacious, it had one virtue; it turned men's minds from the magical aspects of alchemy to a study of chemical reactions and ultimately to chemical analysis.

Another important chemist was Robert Boyle, a contemporary of Stahl, who criticized the concepts of alchemists and metaphysicians in his book *The Skeptical Chymist*, published in 1661. Boyle insisted that the term "element" should be restricted to substances that are irreducible, and he made a clear distinction between elements and compounds. Still another eminent figure was Franciscus Sylvius, head of the first university chemical laboratory at Leiden, Holland, who became a professor in chemistry in 1658. Sylvius rejected all ideas of the occult, and studied the properties of acids and salts. His greatest contribution was his insistence on reason and logic as the only means of solving chemical problems.

The eighteenth century witnessed great advances in chemical knowledge and the final overthrow of medieval chemical concepts. In 1775 Joseph Black, a medical student in Glasgow at the time, demonstrated for the first time by experiments that, far from being a simple element as was generally believed, the atmosphere contained "fixed air" (later called carbon dioxide), which he identified as the same gas as that expelled from the lungs in breathing. Many other chemists, during this century, made contributions of value, but dominating them all was Antoine-Laurent Lavoisier, French chemist, who is regarded as the father of modern chemistry.

Lavoisier (1743–1794) almost single-handedly revolutionized the world of chemistry. He formulated the law of the conservation of matter, holding that matter cannot create itself or disappear, but can only change into other forms. The apparent disappearance of substances when heated, he showed, is caused by their conversion into gases. He introduced exactness into the techniques of chemical experiments, devised new laboratory equipment, and insisted on the use of chemical equations as the language of chemistry. The chemical balance he used in his laboratory is said to have been the most accurate one in Europe at that time. In his *Elementary Treatise on Chemistry*, published in 1789, he presented a complete list of known elements and compounds and substituted an exact terminology for the unscientific phrases which had been used by chemists since the ancient days of alchemy. In addition, he gave the *coup de grâce* to the phlogiston theory by demonstrating that combustion is the result of chemical activity and not the manifestation of a mystic essence. Lavoisier pioneered also in biochemistry (the chemistry of living matter). He was the first to explain respiration as a process of combustion, and he also studied animal heat and the metabolism of living tissue.

Unfortunately for the world of science, Lavoisier met a tragic death at the age of fifty-one. He was guillotined during the Revolutionary Terror in 1794, in Paris. ("The Republic has no need of savants," said the judge at his trial.*) Joseph Louis Lagrange, famous mathematician who was living in Paris at the time, said, "It took but a moment to cut off that head, though a hundred years perhaps will be required to produce another like it." Lavoisier, more than any other chemist, was responsible for transforming chemistry from an empiric technique to an exact science. "Until he entered the field, there was no generalization wide enough to entitle chemistry to be called science." [6]

Another eighteenth-century chemist who made important contributions to the science, though he clung uncompromisingly to the phlogiston theory, was Joseph Priestley, an English pastor. Priestley discovered a gas that he called "dephlogisticated air" but that Lavoisier was later to call "oxygen." Attacked by many Englishmen for his radical political views (he championed the causes of both the French and the American revolutionists), Priestley emi-

---

* Compare the statement of the late General Nikolai Vlasik, head of the Okhrana, former State Security system of Soviet Russia, in explaining, in the early days of the Soviet state, the absence of college-trained men in his organization: "We don't need the rotten intelligentsia." Vlasik himself was so uneducated that he could barely sign his name (*Life*, March 30, 1959, p. 83).

grated in 1794 to America, where he continued his experiments and later discovered carbon monoxide.

The nineteenth century was alive with dramatic advances in theoretical, as well as practical, chemistry. One of the most important contributions was made by John Dalton, an English Quaker, who formulated the law of multiple proportions in 1803. All matter, he claimed, consists of atoms that are alike and have the same weight in each element. Chemical change is caused by the union of atoms of different elements; red powder results from the heating of mercury in the air, because each atom of mercury unites with an atom of oxygen to produce a compound, the red oxide of mercury. Dalton showed that atoms combine in weights proportional to whole numbers, and was the first to draw up a table of atomic weights for different elements. Dalton's ideas were revolutionary for his time, and many years passed before they were universally accepted. As late as in 1868, Charles Eliot, a chemistry teacher who was later to become president of Harvard University, warned his students that "the existence of atoms is itself a hypothesis and not a probable one. All dogmatic assertion upon it is to be regarded with distrust." These words show how far chemical education in the United States has traveled in less than a century—from the Atomic Dispute to the atomic reactor!

With increasing knowledge of atomic weights, chemists began to wonder if there were relationships between the atomic weights and the properties of different elements. Beginning in 1869, Dmitri Ivanovich Mendeleev, a Russian chemist, developed a Periodic Table which not only showed such a relationship but revealed that when the elements were listed in the order of their atomic weights, certain properties recurred periodically, the gaps on the table representing elements that were yet to be discovered. Just as the planet Neptune was discovered by similar "gaps" in astronomical data, so have gallium, germanium, and other elements been unearthed in accordance with Mendeleev's predictions. The latest element to be discovered at this writing has been named "mendelevium," in honor of the Russian chemist. Mendeleev's table was later modified and improved to include elements that could not otherwise fit into it logically.

Until the first quarter of the nineteenth century, an impassable gulf was supposed to exist between the chemistry of living matter and that of inanimate matter. The organic chemical compounds that make up human tissue or body fluids were believed to be of a special kind that could be created only by a "vital force" that animated all living cells. This concept was destroyed for all time in 1828 by Friedrich Wöhler, a German chemist, who transformed an inorganic compound into urea, which is an organic compound. His dramatic demonstration that the chemicals of the body are no different from the same chemicals in dead matter opened up a new chemical era. It led to the synthesizing of countless thousands of organic compounds and the creation of the pharmaceutical industry, with its mass production of synthetic drugs and medicines.

Another fundamental advance came near the end of the century, when startling discoveries were made about the nature of the atom. Wilhelm Konrad Roentgen discovered that solid matter was not so solid after all, since it could be penetrated by radiations that were called X rays. In 1896 came a more significant discovery by Henri Becquerel. He accidentally put a piece of photographic film in a drawer with a sample of uranium salt on top of it. When he developed the film, he was astonished to discover a crude photograph of the uranium, in spite of the fact that it had been separated from the film by black paper. Thus was radioactivity discovered! It was soon after this that Marie and Pierre Curie—most distinguished husband-and-wife team in scientific history—began their long and arduous task of isolating the essential radioactive ingredient from pitch-blende. They finally unearthed two hitherto unknown radioactive elements, polonium and radium. The atoms of these elements were found to have properties that challenged the classic concept of the atom as a stable, indestructible unit of matter. In a single gram of radium, for example, billions of atoms disintegrate every second, giving off alpha rays as they break down into smaller units of matter.

A more serious blow against the then prevalent billiard-ball concept of atoms was delivered in 1897, when new particles forming part of the structure of atoms (later called *electrons*) were discovered in the form of cathode rays. At first a hunch, then a theoretic probability, the existence of electrons was finally established beyond doubt. Trails made by electrons were actually photographed, appearing on the film as skeins of thread. More remarkable still, Robert Millikan later succeeded in removing a single electron from an atom of oil spray by the use of radium.

To account for these and similar phenomena, a revolutionary new theory of the atom was formed and developed in turn by J. J. Thomson, Niels Bohr, and Ernest Rutherford. The atom that finally evolved from their investigation was a miniature solar system, consisting of a central nucleus and varying numbers of electrons that whirl around it at a speed of 160,000 miles per second. The solid, irreducible billiard ball, symbol of the atom since the time of Democritus, over two thousand years ago, had become a philosophic anachronism.

These developments had a revolutionary effect on chemistry as well as on physics. The new electron theory of matter enabled the chemist to understand the actions and reactions of chemicals much more clearly and accurately than before. It helped to solve many riddles: What happens when a substance is dissolved, for example—or when an electric current is passed through a solution? It led to new concepts, new fields of chemistry, further new discoveries and industrial applications.

Chemistry entered the twentieth century solidly established as a major science. It was like a young tree whose richest fruits were yet to blossom but whose roots were deeply anchored. In inorganic chemistry, the foundations of electrochemistry had been laid, based on the study of the effects of electric currents on chemical solutions. Organic chemistry was beginning to expand to new horizons, thanks largely to the discovery of Friedrich Kekule, whose benzene-ring formula helped to explain the structure of thousands of organic compounds. The discovery that in organic compounds atoms occupy different planes of space led to the development of stereochemistry (three-dimensional chemistry). Chemists could predict accurately the results of complicated chemical reactions; they could synthesize many organic compounds; they could tell what elements were yet to be discovered and describe their properties. The electron theory was bringing chemistry closer to physics; increasingly, the chemist had to borrow the tools and concepts of the physicist, not only for research but even for testing and analysis in his laboratory.

The expanding horizons in chemistry and its increasing involvement in manufacture and technology led to growing demands for chemists with adequate training and education. This has resulted in the rise of new chemistry schools and the development of professional courses. The first "teaching laboratory," as it was called, was begun by Justus Liebig, pioneer in organic chemistry, in 1826. Friedrich Wöhler, who synthesized urea, established a teaching laboratory in Göttingen that became internationally famous and attracted students from all over the world—among them Frank Jewett, who was later to become professor of chemistry at Oberlin College, Ohio.

In 1900 chemistry was a thousand light-years removed from alchemy, from which it had sprung; yet its most spectacular achievements were still to come. Chemistry was a fast-growing science; it was yet to become a universally respected profession. The chemical industry was growing in significance and power, but it was still far from being a major industry, and, as yet, spent very little for research and development. Now let us turn to the second half of the twentieth century and take a long look at the chemical profession and industry of today, the subjects of the next chapter.

CHAPTER TWO

The Chemical Profession Today

THE STORY IS TOLD THAT WHEN THE UNITED STATES ENTERED World War I, the Secretary of War was visited by a professor of chemistry who offered the Secretary the services of the chemical profession for the duration. The Secretary thanked him but stated, after consideration, that the War Department already had a chemist on its staff and that no further assistance was required!

The story, while perhaps apocryphal, was, according to Dr. James Bryant Conant, "nevertheless in essence true." [1] It shows how far the chemical profession has traveled since 1917. Recognition by the government of the importance of chemistry today is indicated in part by the fact that ten thousand chemists and chemical engineers are now on the pay roll of Uncle Sam.

At the beginning of the century, chemicals were manufactured by primitive methods, in shabby structures having little resemblance to today's imposing plants. The chemicals were for the most part restricted to staples like sulfuric acid, alkalis, and bleaching powder. Alcohol was produced by the fermentation of vegetables instead of from petroleum, which is the source of half the industrial alcohol made today. Few envisioned even the possibility of such present-day chemical marvels as synthetic rubber. The educated chemist was an oddity—in today's language, an "egghead." The chemist employed in an industrial plant was a laboratory technician rather than a chemist—an "underpaid, ill-respected creature with a pipet in his hand, doing routine analysis." [2] In the entire country, there were only a few thousand chemists; and chemical engineering was yet to be born.

Today, there are over 100,000 chemists and more than 50,000 chemical engineers. They are highly respected as scientists by government and industry, and many are officers and executives of large corporations. The chemical profession has burgeoned into the largest of all scientific professions next to engineering. The majority of academic degrees awarded in all fields of science during the past twenty-five years have been in chemistry. In the words of Dr. Conant, "The growth of the chemical profession within the lifetime of many of us has been one of the amazing social phenomena of our times." [3]

This growth was attended by a phenomenal expansion of the chemical industry. Typical is the life history of the Monsanto Chemical Company. In 1900 this company had only one plant, its equipment consisting largely of rows of wooden tubs—and its sole product was saccharin. Today, Monsanto does a $714,000,000 annual business and its thirty-three plants are scattered throughout the country. These plants manufacture more than a thousand different products, from alcohol, acids, food flavorings, and abrasives to synthetic fibers, plastics, insecticides, fungicides, and pharmaceuticals. In one twenty-five-year period, Monsanto's rate of expansion was 300 per cent greater than the average rate for the entire economy.

A similar story could be told of other major chemical companies. At the beginning of the century, a list of twenty-five of the largest manufacturing corporations in the country would not have included a single chemical company. Today the chemical industry is the fifth largest in the country, with assets of 20 billion dollars. In addition to chemical raw materials, it manufactures countless finished products that it sells directly to the consumer. Moreover, it has penetrated other industries, such as petroleum, metals, and atomic energy, and has improved or transformed their products; it has revolutionized the textile industry by creating new synthetic fibers; it has spawned whole new industries based on man-made chemical materials not found in nature, such as plastics and synthetic rubber. In addition, it has created new consumer needs and requirements; half the chemical sales today are of products that were not even on the market thirty-five years ago.

The chemical industry takes its raw materials from the air, the sea, and the farm, from oil and gas wells, and converts them into some 11,000 chemical compounds in the forms of acids, alkalis, and salts in more than 12,000 plants across the country. These compounds are then transformed into innumerable products and materials vitally needed in manufacturing, transportation, agriculture, biology, and medicine. Chemistry is not only Science but Big Business. In the words of Major General E. F. Bullene, U.S.A.: "The chemical industry today must be reckoned among the greatest industrial forces of all times. It is the nerve center of our entire industrial system. In peacetime, its products are essential to every phase of our daily lives; in wartime, they are indispensable."

As the industry expanded, so did the demand for trained chemists. In time, this demand mushroomed far beyond the requirements of the chemical industry itself. New processing industries sprang up, with their own chemical departments, in which the basic compounds supplied by the chemical plants were converted into such products as paint, rayon, film, rubber, and glass. Oil and gas companies also became makers of chemicals; so did paper manufacturers, producers of electrical machinery, and food processors. More recently, a new trend has appeared—the formation of partnerships between chemical and nonchemical concerns for the manufacture of synthetic fibers, petrochemicals (so-called because they are derived from petroleum), and high-energy fuels.

With the accumulation of new knowledge in one field after another, chemistry became more and more specialized. Even a century ago, it was not easy for a chemist to keep up with developments in all fields. Justus Liebig, noted nineteenth-century German chemist and teacher, once said to his students, "You have to kill yourself with reading to get anywhere in chemistry nowadays." What would Liebig have said if he were alive today and could peruse the pages of *Chemical Abstracts*? This publication, which summarizes reports by chemists all over the world, may have as many as 500 pages of closely packed print in each issue, with two columns on each page. There are 31 main divisions of subject matter, and the articles abstracted are taken from about 5,000 technical journals published in 31 languages. It would be impossible for even the most brilliant chemist to absorb more than a tiny part of this vast flood of knowledge and information. The most he could hope to do would be to keep abreast of developments in his particular field.

As new specialized fields developed, the American Chemical Society, which is the parent organization of professional chemical societies, has been obliged for the last half-century to form one new division after another. The total list is impressive evidence of the vast scope of the chemical profession today. It includes the following fields: agriculture and food; analytical chemistry; biological chemistry; carbohydrates; cellulose; chemical marketing and economics; colloids; fertilizer and soil; gas and fuel; industrial and engineering chemistry; inorganic chemistry; medicinal chemistry; organic chemistry; paint, plastics, and printing ink; petroleum; physical chemistry; polymers; rubber; water, sewerage, and sanitation.

Fifty years ago, the largest group in the profession was that of inorganic chemists. Today, owing to revolutionary developments in various fields of organic chemistry, it is the organic chemists who are by far the most numerous. The percentage of chemists in each branch of chemistry in 1951, the most recent year for which these figures are available, was as follows: [4]

Specialty	Percentage
Organic chemists	46.1%
Analytical chemists	13.3
Inorganic chemists	9.1
Physical chemists	8.0
Biochemists	5.5
Other specialties	18.0

Today, about 80 per cent of all chemists are employed in private industry. The great E. I. du Pont de Nemours & Company, with its widely diversified activities, alone employed 3,900 in 1958. A survey in 1954 showed that the largest group of chemists were employed in the chemical and allied products industries. The next largest were in various manufacturing industries; then came the petroleum, food, primary metal industries, electric equipment and rubber products industries. This list again reflects the great variety of fields that require the services of chemists.[5]

It was research and development that sparked the phenomenal advances of the chemical industry. It has been estimated that, of every dollar representing the sales of chemicals, three cents is spent for research—as against one cent in nonchemical industries. In 1957, one-third of the sales of the Union Carbide Company, one of the giants of the industry, were of products that were completely unknown fifteen years previously. Chemical companies spend many millions in attempts to discover and develop new products and materials—for example, the du Pont Company spent more than 80 million dollars for the development of Dacron, a synthetic fiber. Research is an expensive gamble; of the fifty thousand new chemical compounds that are developed by chemists every year, the great majority never get beyond the research-laboratory stage. The winnings in such gambles, however, are incalculable, and may result not only in vast profits but also in the creation of new industries for the manufacture of new types of materials.

The expenditure of vast sums for research is a comparatively recent industrial development. A graph tracing the amount of money spent by the American chemical industry for this purpose during various periods in the past would start almost at the zero point in 1900 and move up to comparatively high levels in the 1920's. Even in 1930, however, research budgets were relatively modest. Not until the forties did they approach the levels of today. As the budgets increased, the number of research chemists rose until, by 1954, approximately 27,000 chemists were employed in industrial research and development fields alone.[6]

Chemical research requires expensive instruments and equipment. In 1900 a small set of glassware was all that was necessary for a lifetime of study. Even fifty years ago, the chemist had relatively few instruments at his disposal in the laboratory. Thus, when Herbert H. Dow, founder of the Dow Chemical Company, wanted to alert an operator in

Above. An example of teamwork: Research chemists John Thompson (left), Dwight Johnson and Williams Langsdorf thrashing out basic theoretic problems in the process of developing du Pont's Delrin plastic. *(Courtesy E. I. du Pont de Nemours and Company, Inc.) Below.* Research chemist W. G. Guldner with apparatus for measuring the surface area of powdered metals on the basis of the amount of gas absorbed by the particles. *(Courtesy Bell Telephone Laboratories)*

Left. Organic chemist making a study of organic processes by means of radioactive "tracers." *(Courtesy Union Carbide Corporation)*

Below. Two organic chemists analyzing a problem in polymerization. Blackboard and chalk are frequently the chief tools of the research chemist. *(Courtesy Union Carbide Corporation)* his plant, he fixed a wire across a chemical pot, with a weight suspended on one end. When hot fumes from the chemicals burned through the wire, the weights dropped to the floor and the thud warned the operator that it was time to take certain corrective measures. Later, this Rube Goldberg invention was improved and a bell rang instead. Today, an operator is not even needed; the chemicals are analyzed automatically by an infrared spectrometer, and when the slightest change takes place it is relayed electrically to automatic controls that make the necessary adjustments.

While the overwhelming majority of chemists are employed in private industry, as we have seen, about ten thousand chemists and chemical engineers work for Uncle Sam. Contrary to what one might expect, 90 per cent of them are settled, not in Washington, D.C., but in New York and California. Many chemists prefer working for the government because it offers wider opportunities for research than a job in industry. This is especially true of basic research, which is concerned with pure knowledge rather than with practical applications. The atmosphere in a government laboratory is more like that in a university, and its chemists do not work under the pressure that prevails in most industrial laboratories.

The scope of government research projects is very wide, ranging from atomic energy to the development of synthetic drugs and of structural materials from surplus farm products. The Federal laboratories are well equipped with instruments of the most advanced types, including electronic computers. Periodic seminars are conducted, and chemists have opportunities to meet distinguished scientists from foreign countries who frequently visit the laboratories. As a government chemist, you would have ample opportunity for recognition. Your reports would be published in scientific journals and you might be asked to write a book or contribute a chapter to some important scientific work.

The long-term demand for chemists in all fields is expected to rise steadily. Authorities predict there will be increasing opportunities for chemists in the next decade, because of the anticipated growth and expansion of many industries requiring their services, especially the chemical and petroleum industries. The production of chemicals has increased by 10 per cent annually for the past twenty-five years, and the rate of growth is expected to rise even higher by 1980. All through the United States, small as well as medium-sized and large companies are either instituting new research programs or expanding old ones. Apart from these developments, a certain number of chemists are needed simply to replace those who have died, retired, or quit the profession. The number required for replacements only, was 1,200 in 1955, but this figure is expected to become higher with continued expansion of the chemical profession.

While long-term career prospects in the field of chemistry are therefore excellent, the demand for chemists may fluctuate considerably in certain periods. For example, after World War II, the need for chemists rose sharply, owing to the expansion of the chemical and allied industries; by 1955 the demand was so great that one authority referred to it as "frantic." A few years later, it subsided to lower levels, dipping sharply to a new low during the business recession of 1958. Even at the bottom of the recession, however, the relative number of unemployed chemists was not so great as the number reported in other fields.[7]

One important sector of the profession in which supply limps behind demand is college teaching, since there are not enough instructors and professors to meet the need of an expanding school population. Colleges are already becoming overcrowded, and indications are that conditions will get worse; authorities predict that by 1970 the number of enrolled students in our schools will be double the number in 1959. The problem of getting enough chemistry teachers for expanded classes is a serious one. Certainly, here is one field in which chemistry graduates need not fear unemployment.

Unlike the high-school teacher of chemistry, the college professor must be a trained chemist, preferably one with a Ph.D. in chemistry. Not only must he be able to teach; he must also keep up with developments in many fields of chemistry. As one professor explained, "If you are a professor of organic chemistry, for example, one or more of your students will be interested in petroleum or in antibiotics or in textiles . . . and you had better have some idea of what's what in each case." [8] In addition to teaching, college professors may do consulting work for private firms, or engage in research. University laboratories are today the most important centers of basic research in the country, and many have contracts for applied research either with government agencies or with private firms. A 1951 survey showed that more research of this kind was being done in chemistry than in any other scientific field, except in the realm of military research which was dominated by physics. In spite of the fact that chemists earn more in private industry than as teachers in universities, a significant number of chemistry graduates choose teaching as a career, either because they prefer the academic life or because of the greater freedom in research that exists in university laboratories.

The income of chemists compares favorably with that prevailing in other fields of science. It rose considerably after World War II, as the demand for chemists increased, and the highest level was in the 1950's. This is indicated in the chart on page 24, which shows the median monthly

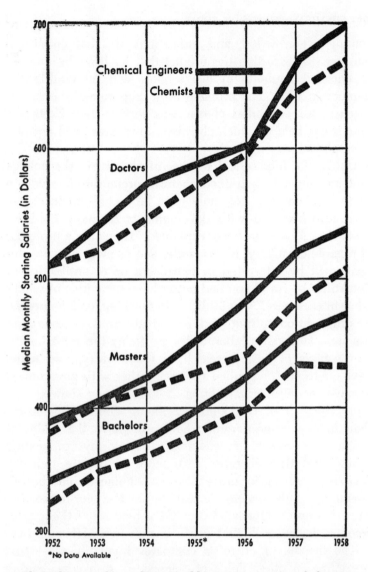

Chart showing the median monthly *starting* income of chemists and chemical engineers for each year from 1952 to 1958. The three pairs of curves show earnings for those with bachelor's degrees, master's degrees and doctor's degrees, respectively.

salaries received by chemists and chemical engineers with different academic degrees, from 1952 to 1958: [9]

In 1958 the median starting salary for B.S. chemists was $440 a month for men and $374 a month for women chemists (an average gain of 35 per cent since 1952). As shown by the chart, graduate training leads to higher income as well as to prestige; chemists with a Ph.D. degree earned $675 compared to $511 for B.S. chemists. The salary for chemistry teachers was comparatively low—$500 a month average for Ph.D. instructors compared to $700 for Ph.D. chemists in industry.[10]

Among industrial chemists, the highest starting salary was received by chemists in the petroleum industry, as shown by the following table: [11]

Industry	Monthly Median Starting Salary
Petroleum	$465
Chemical	450
Plastics	450
Food	420
Biological and pharmaceutical	400

The chemical profession has come a long way since the turn of the century. From a narrow, technical craft it has advanced to the level of a truly scientific profession. Today it is universally recognized for its vast contributions to our national economy. Not only has it created revolutionary new materials and processes but it is also playing a leading role in the new field of atomic energy. Said Dr. Willard F. Libby, member of the Atomic Energy Commission: "The A.E.C. is fully aware of the great contribution American chemistry has made in developing our atomic arsenal and in developing important, peaceful uses, especially isotopes. It looks to the chemical profession for assistance in the future."

CHAPTER THREE

Qualifications and Training

SHOULD YOU BECOME A CHEMIST?
To a young man or woman, the question is as crucial as the more romantic one, "Should I marry Ann (or Joe)?" Indeed, the problem is not altogether dissimilar, for a career may be defined as marriage to a particular profession or trade.

As in marriage, so in choosing a career: you should make sure that the partnership is a congenial one. You should ask yourself two related questions: (1) Have I the necessary traits and qualifications? (2) Would I *like* the work of the chemist? Some people are eminently well qualified for a career in chemistry but would not be happy in a chemist's environment. Other individuals enjoy working in a laboratory with chemicals but do not have the necessary traits or qualifications. For a successful chemical career, you need both the qualifications and the capacity to enjoy the work.

Essentially, the traits required are the same as those needed for any other scientific profession. You must have a liking for science—which means, in the first place, for chemistry and physics. You must be intelligent, observant, alert, imaginative, neat, exact, painstaking, patient, objective, able to work harmoniously with others, to work long hours if necessary and be completely absorbed in your work. Other qualities are needed for specialized fields. The distinguished chemist and Nobel Prize winner Georg von Hevesy added the qualities of enthusiasm, perseverance, and the ability to separate what is important from what is relatively unimportant as attributes of great scientists.[1]

Manual skill is helpful, of course, but not necessary. Young people are sometimes asked: Do you like to build model planes, to develop your own photographic films, to repair radio sets? If the answer is Yes, they are too often told that they are potentially suited for a career in science. Actually, they may be more fitted for a career in mechanics or mechanical engineering. Much more important is the ability to work harmoniously with others, as part of a team. This is essential, even in chemical research. Modern discoveries are usually made, not by lone individuals, as in the nineteenth century, but by groups of chemists and chemical engineers working together. An example of such a discovery is Delrin, the du Pont plastic product. A consideration of how it was discovered and developed will not only illustrate the importance of teamwork but will also indicate the complexities and close interrelationships of chemical research, development, and production.

The story of Delrin begins with basic research. Two du Pont chemists, Hugh Gray and Archie Barkdoll, were studying the chemical reactions of pure formaldehyde, when they discovered that polymers (huge molecules in long chains) of the formaldehyde were created under conditions that seemed unfavorable for their formation. This would appear to be a relatively unimportant observation, but it had tremendous consequences. Its immediate result was an attempt by Robert MacDonald, another chemist in the company, to develop a satisfactory method of synthesizing the polymers. This was successfully accomplished, whereupon a team of chemists and engineers was assembled to determine whether it would be worth while to embark on full-scale commercial production of the plastic. (As we shall see later, all plastics consist of such polymers.) This investigation took years. It involved the preparation of larger quantities of the material in the laboratory for purposes of testing, the development on a small scale of manufacturing processes, and studies of the economic value of the product and of the profits that could probably be derived from its manufacture and sale. During these investigations the size of the research team increased still more, and valuable ideas were contributed by various members of the group. Complex theoretic problems were thrashed out in discussions (see photograph facing page 20). Several kinks had to be ironed out, and it was found that more knowledge of the basic polymer structure of the plastic was needed; chemist Theodore Koch and his group made fresh studies of its molecular properties. Meanwhile, in another group, chemists John Punderson and Steve Dal Nogare developed methods of ensuring its stability at higher temperatures.

After favorable results were obtained in these investigations, engineers constructed a unit to study the process of manufacturing the plastic. Several years were required for design engineers to acquire all the data needed to design the equipment which would be required for a full-scale manufacturing plant. During this time, ideas were contributed by technicians and craftsmen, in addition to chemists and engineers. In this way, hundreds of suggestions were drawn from the rich reservoir of knowledge and experience of the du Pont scientific and technical force, before the new plastic was completely developed and could be placed on the market. This, the reader will agree, was teamwork!

To be a successful chemist, you must also be able to work hard and be absorbed in a project in complete oblivion of the passage of time. To quote Dr. Carroll A. Hochwalt, vice president of the Monsanto Chemical Company: "Just try to recall one eminently successful research chemist who operated on a 9 A.M. to 5 P.M., five-day-a-week schedule! We are not implying that the research chemist should be devoid of other interests in life—far from it!—but, unless he is in love with his work, he is destined to mediocrity."

Many young people, in awe of scientists, have the mistaken belief that chemistry is not for them because they are not mental giants. The truth is that you do not have to be a Lavoisier or a Mendeleev to be qualified for chemistry. Very few scientists in any age are endowed with genius.

Genius is not necessary, but a reasonably high level of intelligence *is*. It is significant that chemists who were in the Armed Forces during the last World War received comparatively high ratings in mental-ability tests. Vocational guidance counselors regard the "intelligence factor" as one of the most important factors in tests designed to determine fitness for a chemist's career. Said Dr. William C. Krathwohl, director of tests at the Institute for Psychological Services at the Illinois Institute of Technology, "If a person wishes to be a chemist and the results of several mental ability tests all show that he is well down the scale, he may still work in the field of chemistry but it should be at the level of the technician."

Great patience and painstaking persistence are other traits needed. Chemists and microbiologists who developed terramycin, the antibiotic, had to study nearly 100,000 molds before they found the one they were seeking. Nor had they any guarantee that they would succeed or that they were on the right path. Indeed, most trails in chemical research lead nowhere, yet each must be thoroughly explored before it is abandoned for another trail.

The late Dr. Laurence Ryden, a young chemist on the research staff of the Dow Chemical Company, had this kind of patience. Given the assignment of developing applications for latex, from which rubber is made, he spent eight long years wrestling with the problem. One day he learned of unsuccessful attempts by German chemists to use latex as a base for paints. Off Ryden went on this new trail, but he too was unsuccessful, and paint experts warned him that his efforts would be fruitless. In the midst of his experiments Ryden was stricken with polio and had to be placed in an iron lung. Though flat on his back, he continued his studies, dictating instructions for fresh experiments. One day he decided that what was needed was a chemical stabilizer. He added this to the latex paint—and soon hit the jackpot. Today the product that he developed is manufactured at the rate of 60,000,000 gallons a year.

Patience is needed also to endure the more prosaic assignments. As a research chemist, you may feel elated at your success in synthesizing a new organic compound—only to learn the following day that your next assignment is a pedestrian one, like improving the process of manufacturing phenol! Chemistry, like engineering, has been glamourized by writers who emphasize the dramatic high lights. The truth is that there are many dull stretches that must be endured with patience and equanimity, just as in any other profession.

To be a successful chemist you must also be open-minded and receptive to new ideas, even though they challenge accepted beliefs. Hundreds of chemical compounds are being manufactured today by processes regarded as impossible thirty years ago. Dr. Edward U. Condon, president of the American Association for the Advancement of Science, stresses the importance of the critical attitude as "an essential ingredient of the scientific method of working." He adds that "conformity, in the sense of uncritical adherence to established doctrine, is a deadening thing to the scientific and intellectual growth on which progress depends." In the same vein, Dr. W. A. Noyes, Jr., of the University of Rochester, urges graduate chemists to cultivate originality and "an investigating, pioneering spirit." [2]

Typifying this spirit and attitude was Svante Arrhenius, the Swedish chemist. As a university student, he informed his chemistry professor one day that he had developed a new theory to explain the ionization of salts in solution. The professor was one of those men who are distrustful and suspicious of new theories. He answered, sarcastically: "You have a theory. Very interesting. Good day, sir!" Today, few people know the name of the professor; that of Arrhenius is famous throughout the scientific world because of this theory of electrolytic dissociation.

One quality that is particularly important for research is the power of deduction—or what is popularly known as imagination. A Swiss biochemist noticed that some people showed signs of being undernourished even though their diet contained sufficient quantities of fats, carbohydrates, and proteins. Pondering on the cause of this, he came up with the startling notion that other, "small quantities of unknown substances" must be present in the food in order to provide proper nourishment. That was in 1881. These substances were later isolated and, in 1911, given the name of "vitamins." To quote Dr. Linus Pauling, Nobel Prize-winning chemist: "Many scientific discoveries, perhaps the most significant ones, represent feats of imagination, insight and originality closely similar to those involved in creative work in such fields as art and music." [3] Students who shy away from chemistry because they regard it as dull and un-creative should ponder these words.

If you are in doubt as to your qualifications for a career in chemistry, you should take aptitude tests to help you decide. More than 500,000 students were given these tests in 1958, and authorities predict that in five years virtually all colleges will require them. An important reason for this is that the National Defense Education Act seeks to make aptitude testing a part of the program in every college, and provides funds for this purpose. The counseling program worked out and used at Pennsylvania State University has been particularly effective in providing proper career guidance.

Aptitude tests are very valuable but, according to author-ities, their limitations should also be kept in mind. Such tests are not infallible, for the human mind is too complex to be measured and analyzed like a machine. Tests cannot fathom a student's "innate intelligence," nor can they meas-ure an individual's motivation, his sense of values, or his ability to work harmoniously with others. For these reasons college officials regard the tests as a secondary rather than a primary criterion in screening students. Some authorities feel that many parents today are misinformed because they have exaggerated notions regarding the ability of aptitude tests to furnish the correct answer.[4]

On the other hand, the results of tests—even conventional examinations—are not without significance. When James McNeill Whistler, the famous artist, was a young man, he flunked out of West Point partly because he had stated in a chemistry examination that silicon is a gas. Many years later, recalling the incident, he said humorously that, be-cause silicon is not a gas, America lost a great general. People who love Whistler's paintings must be correspond-ingly grateful that silicon is a solid!

Once you have decided that you are qualified for a career in chemistry, you should make up your mind whether you want to be a research chemist or work in some other field. As a research chemist, you would have your choice of working for a private concern, for a university, or for the government. University research offers the most freedom in the choice of research projects. In private industry there is greater pressure on the research chemist to meet the requirements of production, though a certain amount of basic research is also done in industrial laboratories.

Many chemists would prefer to do research, for which they may be well qualified, but choose more remunerative positions instead—or jobs in production departments that lead to higher-paying administrative positions. This conflict between the desire for a higher income and the desire to do creative research has been resolved by some of the large companies by the establishment of new programs in their research departments. At du Pont, for example, research chemists have various grades, depending on their competence and experience. The chemist may advance from "junior research associate" to "research associate" and finally to "senior research associate." To quote a du Pont official: "Outstanding scientists receive incomes comparable to those received for administrative positions." Similar programs, establishing new grades with increases in pay for each grade, have been established at the Esso, the Monsanto, and the Dow Chemical corporations.

Research chemists are also receiving more recognition by company officials than they have in the past, and are being increasingly consulted by management. De Witt O. Myatt, manager of development of Atlantic Research Corporation, stated recently: "I anticipate increasing use of senior scientists as direct consultants to top management in the technical aspects of important organizational interests. This may

even develop to the point where . . . company manage-
ments will defer to the judgment of the non-manager scientist." [5]

Educational Requirements

Education for a career in chemistry should begin in high
school, where you should take as many courses in chemistry, physics, and mathematics as possible. A course in
biology is also recommended. This will be especially useful
if you should decide later to specialize in biochemistry.

English composition is also required for admission to a
college course in chemistry because it trains the student to
express his thoughts clearly and logically, an indispensable
quality for effective communication and the writing of reports. Many chemists are deficient in this regard. According to Dr. Ralph L. Shriner, of Iowa State College, the most
serious criticism leveled at chemists with advanced degrees
by employers is that "they don't know how to write." [6] Miss
Madeline D. Warnock, chief of the editorial section at the
United States Army Chemical Corps Laboratories at Fort
Detrick, Maryland, warns that "we have a whole generation
of scientists, highly trained in their professions, many of
whom have little ability to communicate." [7]

You should also take courses in German or French, for
a knowledge of foreign languages enables one to read reports in those languages. Besides, these courses may be
required for a college chemistry course or for advanced
degrees.

Naturally, you should take as much high-school chemistry as possible, not only because it is required for admission to college but also for the reason that studying chemistry
may help you to decide whether or not you like it sufficiently to make it your life career. Physics is almost equally
important; in fact it is indispensable for a career in chem-

istry, especially if you decide to become a physical chemist! Educational authorities point out that students understand chemistry better when they have a knowledge of physics. This was shown by a survey of eight hundred students enrolled in college chemistry courses; students who had taken physics as well as chemistry in high school had higher marks than those who had taken chemistry alone.[8]

The high-school subjects required for admission to college chemistry courses vary for different universities. The high-school student should therefore write to the university of his choice and learn in advance what the entrance requirements are so that he will be sure to take all the courses necessary. Most colleges giving degrees in chemistry require, in addition to other subjects, two years of science, at least two years of mathematics, and four years of English.

Mathematics is of prime importance for a career in chemistry. At some universities, candidates for admission to chemistry schools are given preliminary tests in mathematics to make sure they have a knowledge of the subject. In addition to algebra and trigonometry, students are urged to study analytical geometry and calculus, if possible, as they are necessary for courses in advanced chemistry. To quote an authority: "The liberal use, in modern graduate studies in chemistry, of advanced calculus, and, to a lesser extent, of the concepts of vector analysis, places the student who has not studied these subjects, at a disadvantage." [9]

Let us suppose you have matriculated for a chemistry course at a university. What courses would you study? The curriculum varies slightly at different universities. However, the following are typical of the courses for a B.S. degree in chemistry:

General chemistry; qualitative analysis; quantitative analysis; physical chemistry; organic chemistry; physics; mathematics (including differential and integral calculus); foreign languages; English; cultural subjects. In the final year: advanced chemistry (biochemistry, and so on).

Every chemist must have a B.S. degree as a minimum; however, more and more students in chemistry take graduate courses leading to an M.S. or Ph.D. degree. This is a significant development in the chemical profession. From 1949 to 1955, more doctoral degrees were conferred in chemistry than in any other scientific field. There are even those who take the extreme view that graduate training is indispensable for all chemists, irrespective of the kind of work they do. The following is a recent expression of this attitude:

"Personally, I would not call a chemist with only a B.S. degree either an organic chemist, a physical chemist, an inorganic chemist or an analytical chemist. His qualifications for chemical research are very meagre. A cursory glance around an industrial laboratory is sufficient to convince one that much of the work performed by a B.S. chemist could be performed by any trained high school graduate. Such a chemist is usually directed in his work by a chemist with an advanced degree. . . . It is my personal opinion that only students who are willing and able to take graduate training for advanced degrees should enter the field of chemistry." [10]

This view is an extreme one and would no doubt be disputed by many in the profession; nevertheless, the fact remains that chemists with advanced degrees have distinct advantages and enjoy special privileges. For certain positions, such as university teaching, an M.S. or a Ph.D. degree is an absolute requirement. Even when not specifically required, it gives the chemist more recognition and more opportunity to advance to higher positions on the administrative level. Starting salaries, too, are generally higher for chemists with advanced degrees. This is shown by the following figures, representing the median starting salaries (per month) as reported in a 1956 survey by the American Chemical Society:

Chemists with a B.S. degree only $400
Chemists with an M.S. degree 443
Chemists with a Ph.D. degree 600

While remuneration is important, it should never be the determining factor in the choice of a profession. Much more important is job satisfaction, a love for the work itself and, in the case of chemistry, for the magic of chemicals and their bubbling interactions in retorts and test tubes. Joachim Becker, seventeenth century chemist, had such job satisfaction, though he received very little for his work. Becker wrote:

"The chemists are a strange class of mortals, impelled by an almost insane impulse to seek their pleasure among smoke and vapor, soot and flame, poisons and poverty. Yet, among all these evils, I seem to live so sweetly that may I die if I would change places with the Persian king!"

In the following chapters, we shall discuss the kind of work that the chemist performs in each of the specialized fields of chemistry—organic, inorganic, analytical, biochemical, and physical. The reader should bear in mind that no sharp line of demarcation separates them and that the work of the chemist in any one of these fields may include the functions of other fields.

CHAPTER FOUR

The Organic Chemist

LET US BEGIN WITH ORGANIC CHEMISTS, SINCE THEY CONSTI-
tute by far the largest specialized group in the profession.

Organic chemistry—also called carbon chemistry—is concerned with carbon compounds, just as inorganic chemistry
deals for the most part with noncarbon compounds. Of all
the elements, carbon is by far the most gregarious; for
reasons involving its electronic structure, the carbon atom
acts as if it hated to be alone, and will hook on to any other
atom, including other carbon atoms, and form stable compounds, at the flick of an eyelash. Technical handbooks
today list more than 500,000 organic compounds, about ten
times the number of inorganic compounds. Most of them are
just laboratory curiosities, but chemists are continually
screening them to see whether they can be used for various
purposes.

Organic compounds are the basic components of an almost limitless range of material, both living and nonliving,
including wood, plastics, petroleum, pharmaceuticals, dyes,
drugs, rubber, fabrics, all vegetation and all animal tissue. Thus the scope of the organic chemist is tremendous,

covering a multitude of industrial, agricultural, and medical fields.

When Wöhler converted an inorganic compound into an organic compound for the first time, thus demonstrating that the chemicals in living organisms are the same as those composing dead matter, he opened up exciting new perspectives. If urea can be synthesized, scientists speculated, why not other parts of the living body? Perhaps in time protoplasm itself could be duplicated and rudimentary, single-celled life be created by man, in a test tube! While the synthesis of protoplasm is a dream of the future, thousands of organic compounds have been manufactured since Wöhler's time, and man-made organic drugs and pharmaceuticals have revolutionized the practice of medicine.

As an organic chemist, you would be concerned not only with the kind and number of atoms present in a carbon compound (molecular formula) but also with the arrangement of the atoms—that is, the so-called "structural formula." The molecular formula of table salt, an inorganic compound, is simply NaCl. However, the molecular formula of methane gas, which is an organic compound, is CH_4, but it is generally expressed diagrammatically, to show the arrangements of the atoms in the compound, as follows: *

$$\begin{array}{c} H \\ | \\ H-C-H \\ | \\ H \end{array}$$

This is the *structural* formula. It shows the manner in which the four atoms of hydrogen are linked to the single carbon atom. This is an extremely simple type of organic

---

* This is actually a simplified form. The complete structural formula includes symbols, not shown, to indicate the particular plane in space for each hydrogen atom, in relation to the carbon atom.

compound. Now consider the fact that in other types there may be hundreds of carbon atoms in a single compound; that these atoms may be linked together in any number of rings, chains, or spirals; and that there is no theoretic limit to the number of these chains or rings, and you will understand how complicated is the structure of many organic compounds and why it sometimes takes years for the organic chemist to decipher that structure and establish the relative position of each atom in the compound. The matter is further complicated by the fact that the atoms are generally not in the same plane!

As an organic chemist, you might have to figure out all the possible atom arrangements for a substance having a known molecular formula. The number of organic compounds that can theoretically be synthesized from the chemical ingredients of coal, petroleum, or natural gas is so great, because of the different combinations of atoms possible, that it staggers the imagination. Consider one compound in a series of hydrocarbons known as the paraffins, which has 20 carbon atoms and 42 hydrogen atoms. If you calculated the number of different combinations of these atoms that are theoretically possible, you would find that it would reach 3,000,000! From coal tar, which for generations had been discarded as worthless, chemists derive chemicals from which they can synthesize no fewer than 100,000 different compounds.

Instead of the theoretic approach, you might use the experimental method. Given an organic compound, you would seek to rearrange its atoms into different combinations by means of heat or pressure, which changes its chemical structure—and thus its physical and chemical properties. You might, on the other hand, try to transform simple compounds into complex, organic compounds. It is this kind of transformation that has brought about some of the dramatic episodes in chemical history.

A classic example was the development of coal-tar dyes. In 1856 William Henry Perkin, a chemistry student who was only eighteen at the time, spent his Easter holiday trying to synthesize quinine from aniline, a coal tar. He failed (quinine was synthesized for the first time in 1943); but in the dirty sludge left over from his experiments he discovered a purplish substance that imparted a brilliant mauve color to silk. Thus was the first dye created out of coal tar, from which—as from a magic cornucopia—came later a rich procession of invaluable products, such as dyes, perfumes, explosives, and pharmaceuticals, including the famous sulfa drugs.

Two years later, Perkin, beginning again with coal tar, succeeded in synthesizing alizarin, a dye that had until then been derived exclusively from the madder plant. Even more dramatic was the development of synthetic indigo. The chemical composition and structure of natural indigo had been determined by Adolf Baeyer, a German chemist, after fifteen years of research. When indigo was produced commercially, the once-flourishing natural-indigo industry, which was based on the madder plant, was wiped out completely, an example of the great social and economic repercussions of chemical development. Another consequence was the growth in Germany, before the First World War, of a gigantic synthetic-dye industry. Since unstable dyes are also explosives, Germany entered the war with the greatest potential explosives industry in history.

Instead of trying to create new compounds, you might seek to duplicate the composition of a natural substance. You would first determine the formula, both molecular and structural. This formula would be your architect's blueprint. Such was the method used by Perkin when he sought to synthesize quinine. In the early forties, Dr. Robert B. Woodward and Dr. William E. Doering, two young chemists in their twenties, tried again to duplicate the quinine molecule, which consists of fifty-two atoms of carbon, hydrogen, nitrogen, and oxygen, linked together in a complicated pattern. In 1943, after fourteen months of study and experiments, they succeeded, and the fine, interlaced yellow needles of quinotoxine (from which quinine is derived) emerged from solution before their excited eyes.

The triumph, brilliant though it was, was limited to the research laboratory. Quinine is yet to be produced commercially, and we are still dependent for its supply on the cinchona tree, which grows most plentifully in Java. The danger of this dependence was shown in the last world war when Java was seized by the Japanese and the United States was thus cut off from its main source of supply. Sometime in the future, no doubt, a chemist, following the trail blazed by Woodward and Doering, will discover a solution to the problem that will permit the drug to be produced commercially.

Thousands of drugs have been synthesized by organic chemists employed by medicinal chemical companies. These firms supply the pharmaceutical companies which in turn reduce the drugs to "dosage" quantities in the form of pills and tablets. Some powerful drugs that are made synthetically are not found in nature. On the other hand, the antibiotics are produced by fermentation processes from molds found in the soil, as we shall see in a later chapter. However, even the antibiotics may in time be man-made. In 1957 Dr. John C. Sheehan, Professor of Organic Chemistry at the Massachusetts Institute of Technology, synthesized penicillin from simpler chemicals. Two years later, a team of four British scientists, including one organic chemist and one biochemist, produced various types of penicillin by stopping the fermentation process at certain stages and introducing organic compounds. These new methods have yet to prove their effectiveness; at this writing, the mold-and-fermentation process is still far ahead of all other methods. Nevertheless the ability to synthesize penicillin and other antibiotics and be able to produce them commercially would mark a great advance in medical treatment. The synthetic chemist could then produce new types of penicillin that may be more effective than the kind produced from molds, which is powerless to combat certain resistant disease germs.

The booming demand for the new drugs has resulted in an expansion of the drug industry in recent years and this has in turn stimulated demand for organic chemists and biochemists in this field. Drug sales rose from $300,000,000 before the Second World War to nearly $2,500,000,000 in 1958, and authorities predict that the increase in sales will continue up to 1975. Of special interest to the graduate chemist are the huge research programs conducted by pharmaceutical companies, which in 1958 spent $170,000,000 for this purpose. These companies know from experience that research pays off handsomely—this in spite of the fact that only six out of the hundreds of antibiotics developed in their laboratories in 1958 turned out to be commercially acceptable. When the research chemist does succeed, his success is a resounding one from the business standpoint; it has been estimated that 90 per cent of all drug sales in the next twenty years will be for the new wonder drugs.

As an organic chemist in the pharmaceutical field, your work would consist mainly of synthesizing organic compounds or seeking to isolate the active ingredient of a drug. You would use standard methods for the most part, but occasionally you would have to develop new approaches or techniques to solve particular problems. If you were a graduate chemist, you would start as a lab assistant and might work your way up to the grades of junior chemist, senior chemist, group leader and, finally, research director. Most pharmaceutical companies prefer chemists with at least an M.S. degree and at least three years' experience in their specialized field. In spite of these requirements, average salaries are not so high as in other industrial fields.

Changing the structure of a compound by chemical interaction is only one of several methods of transformation. Another method is "polymerization," the creation of very large molecules out of smaller ones by means of heat, pressure, and the use of catalysts. Polymerization produces new substances not found in nature—plastics, for example. The chemist creates a plastic substance by methods that link together hundreds of molecules of an organic compound (formaldehyde, for example) into a giant molecule called a polymer. All plastic substances, of whatever kind, consist of millions of closely packed polymers.

Plastics were born as the result of an offer made in 1886 of a $10,000 prize for the discovery of an adequate substitute for ivory in billiard balls. John Wesley Hyatt, a printer in Albany, New York, experimented with chemicals in a bid for the prize. One day he chanced to mix camphor with cellulose nitrate, produced by the reaction of nitric acid and cotton linters. The result was celluloid, the first known plastic. The discovery opened up a new field of investigation leading to the development of one new plastic after another. Today we have a booming plastics industry, producing approximately twenty-five different basic plastic raw materials. Plastics have taken the place of wood and metal in thousands of products and appliances and, in the form of synthetic fibers, have successfully invaded the textile field. As a result, polymer chemists, as they are called, are in considerable demand. Authorities predict that as natural supplies of basic raw materials needed for industry become exhausted, the demand for plastic substances to take their place will increase sharply—and so will the need for the services of chemists in this field.

The story of synthetic fibers is a dramatic one. It began with the decision of the E. I. du Pont de Nemours Company in 1927 to finance a basic study of the polymerization process, without regard to any immediate practical application. Dr. Wallace H. Carothers, a young organic chemist, was selected to head the research project. He and his associates conducted experiments for years and studied the process whereby small molecules unite to form giant molecules. They had accumulated a vast amount of theoretical data when, one day, chemist Julian Hill, who was studying a new polymer substance, discovered an interesting fact: when molten, the new substance could be drawn into a thin filament that could be stretched to surprising lengths even after it had cooled. Here was a new material, not found in nature, that seemed to have possibilities as a fiber. Tests showed, however, that the filaments were not strong or elastic enough for textile purposes; also, they softened in hot water. Nevertheless, the discovery opened up a new path of exploration.

The research team synthesized one polymer after another, seeking one that would meet textile requirements. After several years of such searching, they began investigating a family of polymers called "polyamides," which produced a gummy material that was strong, elastic, and pliable. After testing more than a hundred of these polymers, they finally succeeded in developing a material that passed all tests and showed superior qualities as a synthetic fiber. They called it "66," but it was named "Nylon" when du Pont announced the discovery in 1938, eleven years after the project was first begun. (To chemists, it is known as hexamethylenediammoniumadipate!)

Nylon appeared on the market first in the form of tooth-brush bristles, then as hosiery and as a substitute for silk in parachutes during the war when Japanese silk was no longer available. Today, owing to its amazing strength and toughness, Nylon is used in the gears and bearings in ma-chinery, as well as for shirts and boat sails. It is difficult to believe that such a valuable material, capable of so many applications, was derived from such ubiquitous substances as coal, air, and water! *

Inspired by the success of Nylon, polymer chemists turned to other sources, like natural gas and petroleum, for the creation of new synthetic fibers. These later made their appearance on the market with such names as Dacron, Orlon, and so forth. Cotton and wood were used to produce the so-called cellulosics, such as Rayon—but these materials are not regarded as true synthetics, since they begin with natural products in the first place. Cotton retains its top billing among fibers, but synthetic fibers have made im-pressive inroads in the textile market. Dr. G. P. Hoff, of the du Pont Company, said, "The time will come when we can no longer afford to use land to raise cotton for clothing. We'll use it for foodstuffs."

Another major field of activity for organic chemists is the petroleum industry. To the layman, petroleum means fuel—something that is poured into the gas tank of his car to furnish power. To chemists it means that, but much more in addition: a rich source of hundreds of different chemical

---

* Actually there is a complicated sequence of operations and transfor-mations in the process, but this is oversimplified in the public mind. Thus a young lady once sent a torn Nylon stocking to the du Pont Company with a letter in which she complained that the chemists "must have skimped on the coal in this batch!"

compounds needed for industrial, agricultural, and medicinal products. The conversion of crude oil into these compounds constitutes one of the most brilliant achievements of the organic chemist as well as of the chemical engineer. Thanks to this science of conversion, called petrochemistry, chemicals can be produced much more abundantly and cheaply than by other methods. Ethylene gas, for example, which was formerly produced by the fermentation of vegetable matter, is today derived from petroleum. To equal the volume of oil-derived ethylene today, over 2,000,000 acres of vegetables would have to be fermented. A similar story could be told about industrial alcohol, half of which comes from petroleum.

Recently, Imperial Oil, Ltd., of Canada, began operating its new petrochemical plant in Ontario. Into the plant every day come 10,000 barrels of crude oil; out of it go such chemical raw materials as ethylene, propylene, and other organic compounds used in the manufacture of thousands of different products, from synthetic fabrics to plastic piping and antifreeze chemicals. Most plastic materials today are derived from petroleum or from chemicals derived from petroleum.

There was a time when gasoline was squeezed out of petroleum by tedious distillation methods. Then came the age of automobiles, with their insatiable hunger for gas. Oil refiners could not meet the expanded demand with these primitive methods. Chemists and chemical engineers were called in to step up production. In 1913 the Burton thermal cracking process was introduced. By means of high temperatures and pressures, the larger molecules of crude oil were cracked into smaller, gasoline molecules. The Burton process increased enormously the proportion of gasoline that could be derived from a barrel of crude oil. Another method developed by chemists was that of polymerization, mentioned before in the discussion of plastics. By means of polymerization, which is the reverse of the cracking process, small, "unsaturated" hydrocarbon molecules are converted under heat and pressure into larger gasoline molecules.

Thanks to the chemist, gasoline is today tailor-made to meet requirements. The type used for driving at high altitudes is different from the type needed for low altitudes; otherwise the gasoline would evaporate in the tank, owing to the lower vaporization point of gas at higher altitudes. (High-altitude gas is made by eliminating the smaller hydrocarbon molecules, since they evaporate readily, and replacing them with larger hydrocarbon molecules.) Different kinds of gas are used by motorists for winter and summer driving. Chemists have also eliminated engine-knocking caused by uncontrolled combustion. Since knocking is more pronounced when the carbon atoms are linked together in straight chains, chemists alter the gasoline's molecular structure by chemical and physical processes so that the atoms are linked in branched chains instead.

Chemists have developed other fuels from crude oil—natural gas, for example. The gas is compressed into a liquid and stored in steel cylinders for easy transportation into rural regions not served by conventional gas lines. The user can restore it to its gaseous state simply by releasing the pressure to which it has been subjected. Then there are lubricants, needed for countless types of machinery to reduce the wear and tear between moving parts. Practically all lubricants are derived from crude oil. Petroleum chemists can modify their properties to suit various requirements.

Petroleum chemistry has come a long way since 1900. At that time the biggest petroleum research staff in the country included only three chemists; in 1955 there were 2,300 chemists employed in the oil industry. At the beginning of the century, chemical engineering was not yet born as a profession; today more than half the petroleum engineers employed in research are chemical engineers. (The work of the chemical engineer, as distinct from that of the chemist, will be described in a later chapter.)

Petroleum-industry leaders recognize the importance of research, as shown by the $157,000,000 spent for this purpose in 1955 by 75 oil companies. Of particular significance are the increased expenditures for basic, as opposed to applied, research—an increase in 1955 of almost 17 per cent over the previous year. Not only has research been stepped up but new processes involving the use of atomic energy and automation have been introduced. Today petroleum scientists explore for oil with the aid of gamma rays, inspect welds in metal with iridium 192, measure the flow of catalysts in refineries with radiation-detection devices. Chemists and physicists are investigating the use of radiation as a catalyst, to promote chemical reactions in the refinery, as we shall show in a later chapter. All these developments spell new opportunities for qualified chemists. In 1954 the petroleum and petroleum products industries employed 5,600 chemists—more than were employed in any other industrial field except the chemical and allied products industry.

Another area that offers interesting careers to organic chemists is the synthetic-rubber industry. Natural rubber comes from rubber trees tapped in the jungles of Malaya. It is an important industrial material, and when Japan blocked shipments of rubber from the East Indies during World War II, she struck a serious blow at our economy. Research chemists and chemical engineers were assigned the urgent task of making synthetic rubber in sufficient quantities to meet war demands.

The chemists began with the knowledge that natural rubber is a hydrocarbon having the formula C_5H_8 (known as an isoprene). In natural rubber the isoprenes are linked together in long chains forming a giant molecule. It was easy enough for the chemists to develop isoprenes from the hydrocarbon molecules in petroleum, but they could not succeed in polymerizing the isoprenes into the giant molecules of natural rubber. They therefore sought another hydrocarbon molecule in place of the isoprene and finally found it in butadiene. When mixed with styrene, which is derived from benzene, and heated, the butadiene is transformed into a synthetic rubber popularly known as Buna-S. This material proved to be superior even to natural rubber for many purposes and is today used in vast quantities in industry and transportation.

As a rubber chemist, your work would include the preparation and testing of various types of synthetic rubber. You might perform research experiments with different petroleum hydrocarbons and seek to develop new rubber materials for specific uses. In 1957 there were 3,400 chemists employed in the rubber industry.

Another major field of employment for organic chemists is in agriculture. Agricultural chemistry was founded principally by Justus von Liebig, nineteenth-century German chemist, who made important studies of the chemistry of soils and fertilizers. He discovered that plants cannot grow and flourish without sufficient quantities of nitrogen, phosphorus, potassium, and other elements, in addition to water and carbon dioxide. Agriculture has passed through many changes since Liebig's time, but the most revolutionary have taken place in the last thirty years. This has been due partly to mechanization and partly to new biological methods of improving the quantity and quality of livestock, such as crossbreeding. But the most important factor has been the widespread use of different kinds of agricultural chemicals. This is a comparatively recent development; at the beginning of World War II, only fifty basic chemicals were used by farmers, but today more than two hundred are employed—and 80 per cent of them were not even known or available in the early 1940's.

One of the most important uses of agricultural chemicals is for fertilizer. Until 1900, about 90 per cent of all commercial fertilizers were supplied by animal and vegetable wastes; today 98 per cent is furnished by chemical companies in the form of "anhydrous ammonia," a chemical rich in nitrogen, which is indispensable for plant growth, along with phosphorus and potash. Other chemical sources of fertilizers have more recently been developed by organic chemists. They have discovered that urea, when sprayed on fruit trees and vegetable crops, delivers nitrogen as effectively as fertilizer does when mixed with the soil.

In addition to such basic chemicals, organic chemists have developed special farm chemicals, such as insecticides and herbicides, which protect crops against disease and destruction by pests and insects. New and better chemicals for various purposes are coming out of laboratories and chemical plants at such a fast rate that, in the words of one authority, "The miraculous is becoming commonplace." [1] Consider the insect killers called organic phosphates, which were developed to destroy insects that were resistant to DDT. One type is either applied directly to poultry and cattle or sprayed by plane over populated areas; it is harmful only to insects. More impressive still are the so-called "systemic" insecticides. When applied to the seed of a plant, these chemicals work their way up the plant, inside the stems. They are deadly to the insect that feeds on the plant but do not harm the plant itself—nor are they injurious to birds or to certain insects that prey on other insects! Most of these new chemicals are only in the experimental stage of development, but a considerable number are already on the market.

Weeds—for centuries the bane of farmers—are also succumbing to the power of chemicals. One type of herbicide eradicates not only the weed but the roots as well. It also destroys the unwanted leaves of cotton plants, thus making the harvesting of cotton that much easier. Herbicides may even eliminate the need for mechanical mowing of sloped land and irrigation ditches by inhibiting the growth of weedy vegetation. Other chemicals destroy fungus spores, another plague to the farmer. After three years of experimentation, one new chemical shows promise of being able to destroy the scabs on apples and pears growing on their trees—and similar stories could be told of many other new chemicals.

Organic chemists do more than boost the yield and quality of crops; they help to dispose of surplus products. Surpluses have always been a nightmare to the farmer, threatening him with financial loss by driving farm prices down to ruinous levels. Heretofore, the only solution has been a destructive one—the burning of wheat or the plowing under of every third row of cotton. Research chemists have developed a saner method, "chemurgy"—the transformation of farm surplus into valuable industrial products. Father of chemurgy was Dr. George Washington Carver, a self-educated Negro, who was born a slave in the South. Dr. Carver transformed peanuts into no less than three hundred different products, including coffee, bleach, shaving cream, and synthetic rubber. He made rope and fiber rugs from cotton stalks and over one hundred products out of sweet potatoes.

Consider the corn surplus, which amounted in 1957 to more than 1.4 billion bushels, an all-time record. Chemists of the Department of Agriculture developed a process of converting corn into plastics, paper, glue, and many other products of value to industry. It has been estimated that

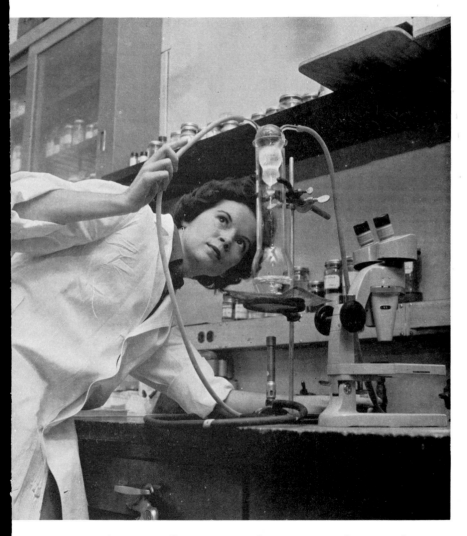

Inorganic chemist Lucille Finneran making a test to determine the durability of glass in alkaline solutions. *(Courtesy Bell Telephone Laboratories)*

Inorganic chemist Ted McKinley testing titanium crystals. He was the first chemist on the du Pont staff to perform research on titanium metal. *(Courtesy E. 1. du Pont de Nemours and Company, Inc.)*

Using the spectrograph to make qualitative and quantitative analyses of materials. *(Courtesy Bell Telephone Laboratories)*

industrial companies could use annually as much as 1.3 billion bushels of corn for these purposes. In an experimental project in the Midwest, thirty thousand acres of special varieties of corn were grown to satisfy industrial needs. While this promises well for the future, authorities state that much more basic research is needed before chemurgy can be practiced on a large commercial scale. More and more, the importance of the problem is being recognized. To quote chemist Roy L. Whister: "The experimental stations at the universities are waking up to the fact that it isn't enough to tell the farmers how to grow more. They have to be told what to do with the crops they have grown."

In this vital area, the organic chemist plays an important role. He has been called the link between the farmer and industry because, in the words of an authority, "He can turn waste products into plastics, synthetic fibers, paints, paper and other products. Putting organic chemistry to work in this manner not only aids the farmer but conserves diminishing natural resources." [2]

As an agricultural chemist, you might prefer working for Uncle Sam. In 1957 about 710 chemists were employed by the Department of Agriculture. Their annual salaries were as follows, in 1959:

Grade	Entrance Salary	Periodic Increase	Maximum Base Salary
GS-5 (junior chemist with a B.S.)	$4,490	$150	$4,940
GS-7 (assistant chemist with an M.S.)	5,430	150	5,880
GS-11 (chemist with a Ph.D.)	7,510	240	8,230

Government salaries are lower than those in private industry. In spite of this fact, many chemists prefer government employment, which offers not only greater security and tenure but also broader opportunities for study and research, as noted in Chapter Two.

So far, we have peered into the wonders performed by the organic chemist in the dye, drug, plastics, textile, petroleum, rubber, and agricultural industries. All these are practical contributions that have added to man's comfort, convenience, and well-being. More important than these practical considerations, however—indeed, basic to them— are the chemist's contributions to our fundamental knowledge and understanding of the processes of nature. This is the primary objective of the chemical research scientist. In the words of Mario Scalera:

"There is no practical purpose here. There is simply man's insatiable curiosity, his abhorrence of the unknown— the desire to see, in the confusing phenomena of nature, the law, the order, that underlies them. This kind of urge has its own reward . . . the reward that comes to a man who suddenly sees order shaping out of chaos—this is what we call fundamental research." [3]

CHAPTER FIVE

The Inorganic Chemist

THE INORGANIC CHEMIST DEALS WITH CHEMICAL COMPOUNDS that, for the most part, contain no carbon atoms. Though the number of known inorganic compounds is much smaller than that of organic compounds, they are of basic importance to industry. Without them, there would be no glass, metals, cement, or concrete, or the innumerable machines and products that require these chemicals for their manufacture, including many organic products as well.

Let us consider phosphorus as an example. Phosphorus was discovered in 1669 by Hennig Brandt, an alchemist, in the course of his experiments. One day he noticed something yellow dripping from the spout of a retort in his laboratory. It glowed in the dark with an eerie light and burst unexpectedly into spitting flame. Brandt christened the new substance "phosphorus," meaning the bearer of light.

Most people think of phosphorus solely in connection with matches, unaware of the fact that it is a vital material in industry and agriculture. Industries served by phosphorus and its compounds include ceramics, oil drilling, pharmaceuticals, leather tanning, textiles, and dyeing. It is also an important ingredient of foods, medicines, dentifrices, and fertilizers. Phosphorus compounds are easily available, for they exist everywhere—in rocks, river silt, animal tissue, and sea water. However, it was not until about thirty years ago that chemical engineers of the Monsanto Chemical Company first succeeded in extracting, refining, and producing phosphorus on a commercial scale. The Monsanto plant in Tennessee, which is the largest in the world, did not have far to go for its raw material. The reddish-brown Tennessee earth, rich in phosphate rock deposits, is waiting to be scooped up by steam shovels and transported in huge ore trucks to the plant. The phosphorus is extracted as a result of the chemical interaction of phosphate rock, coke, and sand. The rock, subjected to high temperatures in an electric furnace, is reduced by the coke to elemental phosphorus in vapor form. The vapor condenses to a syrupy liquid which drips from furnaces three stories high, just as it had dripped from Brandt's retort almost three hundred years ago!

As with phosphorus, so with other inorganic elements: they are the basic ingredients of many substances used in manufacturing, agriculture, and medicine. Consider chlorine, for example. In the old days chlorine had only a few restricted uses; today it is an essential ingredient of scores of products, from DDT to chlorinated rubber and paraffin. Elements that were only laboratory curiosities fifty years ago have today become extremely valuable—for example, fluorine, which was first isolated in 1886 and is today used in plastic materials and in rockets.

So far, we have been discussing the chemical raw materials of industry. As an inorganic chemist, you might be employed in this field. On the other hand, you might be employed instead in the manufacture of products such as metals, glass, ceramics, or foodstuffs. Consider the metals industry. Chemists as well as metallurgists were responsible for making steel harder, tougher, and more resistant to corrosion. One method used to accomplish this is to add manganese or nickel to molten steel, which not only makes the steel harder but also removes impurities from the metal by absorbing oxygen and sulfur. It is for this reason that when tough metal is needed—as for instance in construction equipment—manganese steel alloy is generally preferred.

The development of the high-temperature electric furnace resulted in the development of new metal alloys that could not be produced in conventional coal-burning furnaces—among them chrome steel (which is stainless and tarnish-proof), tungsten, vanadium, and molybdenum steel. Tungsten has a higher melting point than any other metal and is therefore used in the turbojet engines of aircraft. Combined with steel, it produces an alloy so diamond-hard that it is used to machine other metals.

The field of metallurgy has been revolutionized in the last thirty years by the introduction of new metals that were formerly only scientific oddities—titanium, silicon, lithium, germanium. Titanium, discovered in 1789, was first produced commercially about twenty years ago, when chemists and chemical engineers developed methods of separating it from its ore and of reducing the metal to a pure form. The ore is treated with chlorine, and liquid manganese or sodium is added. What results is a sponge-like material containing titanium; this is refined until pure ingots of titanium are obtained. The heat-resistant quality of titanium makes it valuable for supersonic planes and jet engines. It is used also in the steel industry as a purifying agent because of its unusual ability to unite with impurities so that they can easily be removed. As a metal chemist, you might also investigate the properties of silicon, which endows steel with unusual magnetic and electrical properties. Silicon steel is for this reason an excellent metal for electrical equipment.

Chemists have also helped to develop thorium, uranium, and lithium for atomic-energy applications. Lithium, lightest of all metals, combines readily with water to produce hydrogen; it is the chief source of tritium, an isotope of hydrogen that is a chief ingredient of the hydrogen bomb, and is used in the manufacture of pharmaceuticals and ceramics.

Most metals come from ores buried in the earth, but magnesium exists abundantly in the seas and oceans. At Freeport, Texas, chemists and engineers of the Dow Chemical Company extract the metal from sea water. This is a complicated process which begins with the dredging of the Gulf of Mexico for oyster shells. The shells are used for lime which, mixed with magnesium chloride in the water, forms magnesium hydroxide. After many chemical stages and transformations, magnesium is extracted by an electrolytic process. Magnesium is used in the manufacture of airplanes and has many other important applications.

Inorganic chemists are being used increasingly in the metal industry to develop and improve metals by chemical processes. In many cases they are replacing metallurgists, to a limited extent, with chemists. For example, ten years ago few members of the research staff of the Crucible Steel Company were chemists or chemical engineers, and over 90 per cent of its technical personnel were classified as metallurgists. Today 20 per cent are either chemists or chemical engineers, and authorities predict that in the foreseeable future the number of chemical engineers employed by the company will equal the number of all other employed engineers combined.

Behind this trend is the realization by industrial leaders

that problems involving new specialty steels or high-temperature alloys cannot be solved completely by classical metallurgical concepts. Because of the new demands placed on metals in our jet-plane, missile, and artificial-satellite age, basic studies of chemical composition are needed as never before. Consider the problem of stress, which causes corrosion in steel and eventually cracking of the metal. Chemists discovered that the corrosion and cracking are caused to a large extent by the presence of hydrogen in the molten steel, a fact that was not widely known until 1940. By eliminating the hydrogen or by casting the steel in a vacuum, steelmakers have succeeded in reducing the rate of corrosion.

Chemists have discovered also that pure oxygen speeds up the process of refining iron to steel. In 1957 the Jones and Loughlin Company introduced a new oxygen process in their steel plant. In this plant the hot metal, after leaving the blast furnace, goes to an oxygen furnace to be charged with oxygen. Chemists and chemical engineers have also developed a new process that may supplant the conventional smelting process of reducing iron ore to iron, a costly method requiring very high temperatures. Their "direct hydrogen reduction process" is similar to the method used in the petroleum industry to reduce complex compounds to simpler ones and is expected to be more effective as well as more economical than the conventional smelting method. In short, chemists, who used to play only a minor role in the steel industry, are today making major contributions that are supplanting long-established metallurgical methods. The reason was tersely expressed by one authority in these words: "Chemists can change matter; metallurgists cannot." [1]

A major problem in metallurgy is that of corrosion, which causes tremendous financial losses each year. In 1950 it resulted in an estimated 6 billion dollars' worth of damage in the United States alone. If you specialized in corrosion problems as a metal chemist, your experiences might be similar to those of Bill Ashbaugh, who received a degree in chemistry from Albion College in 1948. Employed by the Union Carbide Company, he sought to discover why a particular copper acid unit kept corroding, in spite of the fact that it was designed to be impervious to the acid used. After numerous tests, he and his associates discovered that the trouble was caused by an escape of oxygen which oxidized the copper. An alloy was substituted for the copper, and the corrosion ceased because the alloy was not affected by oxygen. This incident caused Ashbaugh to become interested in corrosion problems. He took special courses in the subject, and soon began developing new methods of tracking down the chemical culprit. Today he is recognized as an authority on corrosion in the chemical industry.[2]

Paralleling the revolution in metals has been the revolution in glass. The history of glass is an ancient one, but though glass was made thousands of years ago, only in the present century have chemists and physicists been able truly to understand its properties and exploit its possibilities. Glass seems to be a solid, but actually it is a supercooled liquid, and is made of fused inorganic materials.

The first glass furnaces were volcanoes, which produced the natural black glass that geologists call obsidian. The art of glassmaking changed little from ancient times to the nineteenth century (even today the glass used in the manufacture of bottles consists of the same chemicals as those used by glass manufacturers in Rome in the first century of the Christian era). In the last fifty years, however, new discoveries and applications have revolutionized the glass industry and transformed it, as tens of thousands of different glass compositions were developed, including almost every element found in nature. The Corning Glass Works alone has more than 65,000 glassmaking formulae. Its technicians melt some 200 new types every week in experiments designed to develop better products and new applications of the material.

Modern glass has hundreds of uses, and its chemical composition can be tailored to meet specific requirements. For laboratory glassware and high-temperature thermometers, for example, the chemical compound borosilicate is used because of its high resistance to heat and its chemical stability. On the other hand, for glass designed to absorb radiation, soda, lime, and lead must be used; cast in massive slabs, such glass constitutes an excellent shielding against radioactivity in nuclear laboratories. The chief ingredients required for optical glass or lenses are borosilicate, soda-lime, and lead. Various colors can be produced by the addition of metal oxides. For example, nickel or cobalt oxide creates a purple color; copper or chromium oxide, a greenish color, and so forth.

The ministrations of the modern chemist and physicist have not only improved the qualities of glass but have also transformed it into completely new forms. Take, for example, fiberglass. It can be bent like rubber or twisted and woven like linen. It is made of the same chemical ingredients as ordinary glass; however, while in a molten state it is made to flow through tiny holes in the base of the furnace and emerges in the form of filaments which are gathered into strands by high-speed winders. Fiberglass can actually be spun and woven on standard textile machinery—yet its tensile strength is as great as that of steel! It is used in the manufacture of insulators, oil-stove wicks, and decorative fabrics. Another remarkable "glass" is Foamglas. Containing 5,000,000 air cells per cubic foot, it can be sawed like wood, and floats like a cork. Foamglas is used in refrigerators as insulation against heat and in life preservers as a substitute for cork.

As a glass chemist, you might be engaged in either basic or applied research. You would study the effects of high-energy radiation on glass samples, as well as their photochemical reactions. Using the electron microscope, you would study the reactions of glass surfaces—an important factor, for it is the surface that chiefly determines the degree of strength and durability of a glass sample. You might be asked to analyze the "batch" (mixture of raw materials fed to the furnace) and study its actions in the melting process and the relationship between these reactions and the chemical properties of the glass. By applying basic chemical concepts, you would seek to expand the uses of the material in industry and in the home.

When chemist James F. Hyde graduated from Harvard, he was employed by the Corning Glass Works to investigate the possibility of creating a new material that would combine the properties of plastics with those of glass. He and Winton Patnode of the General Electric Company laboratories, working independently, finally developed amazing materials called silicones which are actually hybrids of inorganic glass and organic plastics. Most chemists had believed that such a hybrid could not possibly be created.[3] Silicones are fairly new to industry but have shown unusual value for waterproofing paper, textiles, and building materials, and also as polishing and defoaming agents.

Glass chemistry offers an interesting career to the graduate chemist and good prospects of employment. The Corning Glass Works alone employs about one hundred chemists and chemical engineers in production and research. They melt up to forty new compositions daily in a continual search for new and better glass for a variety of purposes.

The vast number of formulae in the Corning files testifies to the amazing number of types and transformations possible in this versatile material.

Inorganic chemists are also in demand in another basic field, the cement industry, which furnishes concrete for streets, highways, bridges, dams, buildings, and structures of all kinds. Portland cement (which constitutes 98 per cent of all cement made) is the chief ingredient of concrete. Chemists analyze the materials, including limestone, clay, and shale, that go into the gigantic revolving kilns, where they are subjected to temperatures of more than 2,700 degrees F. Throughout the process of manufacturing, they take hourly samples and analyze them, to ensure accurate blending. They must exercise strict chemical control of the materials, for the finished cement must meet many chemical and physical specifications before it is delivered. You might be employed in the cement research and development laboratories of the Portland Cement Association, near Chicago —the largest laboratories of this kind in the world. The contributions of research chemists in these and similar laboratories have resulted in the creation of concrete pavement and structures with greater durability than ever before.

A particularly dramatic new field of activity for inorganic chemists just now is that of propellants or rocket fuels for missiles, satellites, and space vehicles. A rocket fuel is a combination of a combustible material and a chemical that oxidizes it (kerosene and oxygen, for example). The rocket engine is really a chemical process plant in which a large quantity of fuel, either solid or liquid, is rapidly converted into hot gases at a precise rate that is automatically controlled. To develop the proper types of propellants, and evaluate them, is the job of the chemist. For such work, he must understand and apply the laws of thermodynamics, kinetics, and heat transfer. He must work in close association with physical chemists and chemical engineers, whose work will be described in later chapters.

The eyes of the world are on the scientists and engineers responsible for the launching of missiles and artificial satellites. In this field of activity, the inorganic chemist plays an important part, for the future of space travel depends to a large extent on the development of better rocket fuels. The space fuel of the future will have minimum weight with maximum thrust power; it will have greater stability, will be more dependable in operation, and will cost less than today's propellants. Here is a unique challenge to chemists and engineers. If they can develop such fuels and improve the pump-fed liquid propellants that are used in most large missiles today, and the solid fuels also used in some rockets and missiles, they will be bringing the age of interplanetary space travel and the discovery of new worlds that much closer to realization.

Chemists are experimenting with fluorine as a fuel. Fluorine is difficult to handle, for it explodes on contact with water and is terribly corrosive. For these reasons it has usually been shipped in small amounts. However, it was realized that if fluorine could be tamed and used commercially as an oxidizer in place of oxygen, it would make rockets soar faster and farther, and satellites larger than any existing ones could be placed in orbit. In 1958 the Bell Aircraft Company reported that its chemists had succeeded in taming fluorine. A new method of handling it in liquid form was developed by the Allied Chemical Corporation, and it can now be transported safely in tonnage quantities to missile research centers.

Solid or liquid propellants? This has become a basic question in rocketry today. Most big rockets use liquid fuels because they produce great thrust in relation to weight. On the other hand, they are dangerous to handle, and require a complicated system of tanks, valves, and pumps. Solid fuel lacks the power of liquid fuels, but it is simpler and safer to handle. Rocket authorities are confident that both types can be improved. Companies are experimenting with different kinds of propellants; one company has reported that its scientists have developed a new type of liquid fuel, based on boron, that is twice as powerful as present-day types.

In the words of Dr. R. J. Thompson, Jr., a propellant chemist: "The chemist will need to apply all his skill, ingenuity and equipment in achieving the advances in propellant technology that will reduce these theoretical improvements to practice and thus provide the propulsive power required for our future exploration of outer space."[4] He adds that the full potential of the chemical rocket "is still far from being realized in practice."

As a propellant chemist, your career might parallel that of Dr. Thompson himself. After obtaining a B.S. degree in chemistry in 1940, he took graduate courses in inorganic and physical chemistry and received a Ph.D. degree from the University of Rochester six years later. Most of his career since that time has been devoted to a study of rocket fuels. Dr. Thompson advanced from one position to another until he became manager of propellant-chemistry research at North American Aviation, Inc.

We have discussed the work of the inorganic chemist to illustrate its practical importance and influence on our industrial economy. Even more significant, however, are the contributions of inorganic chemists to our fundamental knowledge and understanding of the processes of nature. Until thirty years ago, inorganic chemistry had the reputation of being a duller field of study than organic chemistry. Students regarded it as offering far less challenge and scope for research. As a result, relatively few graduate chemists specialized in this field. When atomic-energy projects, requiring the services of inorganic chemists, were initiated, few chemists could be found with the necessary background and training for work on these projects.[5]

Inorganic chemistry was indeed a comparatively static field until the beginning of the twentieth century. Then came such fundamental new discoveries as the quantum theory; new types of chemical reactions based on radioactivity ("hot atom" chemistry);[6] discoveries in the chemistry of high-speed reactions and in high-temperature chemistry; the creation of synthetic elements not found in nature. The new discoveries had practical as well as theoretic importance. For example, complex reactions that were formerly regarded as practically instantaneous can now be broken down into a series of separate steps. On the one hand, this gives the chemist added knowledge and understanding of these reactions; on the other hand, a stream of burning gas can now be tapped at various points and the intermediate products of combustion, consisting of valuable chemicals, can be piped off.

By the method of "ion exchange," the inorganic chemist can even emulate the organic chemist and transform one (inorganic) compound into another. Thus, potassium chloride can be converted into sodium chloride by placing a solution of it in contact with an ion exchanger containing sodium ions (electrically charged atoms). The sodium ions change places with the potassium ions, resulting in the formation of sodium chloride. The same technique is used to soften water. What makes water hard are the ions of calcium and magnesium in it. These ions are replaced by sodium ions in ion-exchange columns through which the hard water is made to pass, and the water becomes soft. In the Metropolitan Water District of Southern California is the largest ion-exchange water-softening plant in the world, treating an average of 140,000,000 gallons of water a day.

Ion-exchange has other commercial applications, such as removing impurities from water and salts from beet juice in the making of sugar. However, its industrial applications are as yet limited. As a research chemist in this field, you might develop them further, for the theoretic possibilities are fascinating to contemplate. Perhaps someday gold or uranium will be extracted from sea water by this method. The new technique might even revolutionize the metal-mining industries. Solvent solutions may someday be sent underground, instead of miners, and the metal to be mined will be extracted from its ore by the method of ion exchange.[7]

We have given the reader a glimpse of some of the exciting new developments in inorganic chemistry. They are often referred to by writers as examples of "modern alchemy." Some chemists question the use of this expression, as it implies a link between medieval magic and modern chemistry which does not in fact exist. The truth of the matter is that the synthesis of new elements that are not found in nature, and the transformation of one inorganic element or compound into another, are achievements that dwarf even the dazzling dreams of the alchemists.

CHAPTER SIX

The Analytical Chemist

As an analytical chemist, your basic function would be to analyze samples of materials, both qualitatively and quantitatively, and determine their chemical composition and structure. This is fundamental for all chemical operations, whether in production, development, or research. The question "What is it made of?" in the chemical field is as central as the question "Who dunnit?" in a mystery thriller. Indeed, the analytical chemist has often been referred to as a chemical detective. His ability to answer these questions is, to a large extent, the secret of modern industrial progress. As one authority put it, "Without the science of analytical chemistry, our basic industries would never have developed to their present state." [1]

The analyst has other duties as well. He must determine to what extent chemicals deteriorate when stored. He must prepare and standardize reagents (substances used as known standards against which the properties of other substances are measured); determine the melting and boiling points and other properties of solids, liquids, and gases; and design and construct apparatus needed for analysis.

The term "analytical chemistry" was originally coined by Robert Boyle (1627–1691), who was one of the first scientists to define an element as a chemically irreducible substance and to make clear the distinction between an element and a compound. However, unlike other chemical fields, analytical chemistry is not associated with any one historical figure—as organic chemistry is with Wöhler, for example. It developed on the basis of the accumulated contributions of countless obscure and little-known chemists, as well as of famed scientists like Boyle and Lavoisier.

Until the twentieth century, the work of the analytical chemist was largely cut-and-dried and consisted of chores that could be done for the most part by laboratory technicians. Complex substances were broken down into simpler, recognizable compounds by standardized processes that required little imagination to perform. Some of the methods used then are still widely employed today—for example, titration, a method of determining the exact amount of a substance in solution by the use of a standard reagent solution. The analytical chemist still uses traditional reagents; their reactions with unknown substances reveal the chemical identity of these substances just as they did a century ago. However, for the analysis of more complicated mixtures of compounds these methods have been superseded by the use of new instruments and techniques that have revolutionized analytical chemistry, making it much speedier, more dependable, and more precise.

Consider the problem of analyzing the various components of petroleum, for example. It would take a chemist an entire day to determine the nature and amounts of seven of these components, if he used the classical methods of analysis. By means of infrared spectroscopy, he can perform the operation in less than an hour.[2]

The graduate chemist soon learns that in many cases no

single machine or technique can give him all the information he wants about a mixture of organic compounds. Each provides a set of clues, and the more instruments of different kinds that are used, the more complete is the analytical picture. Nevertheless, the speed and dependability of these machines are remarkable. Consider the infrared spectrophotometer. The chemist places the unknown sample to be analyzed into the instrument, where it is exposed to infrared radiations. Different wave lengths of the infrared will be either transmitted or absorbed by the sample, depending on its chemical composition. The transmission and absorption effects are translated into electrical impulses that are recorded on a chart on a revolving drum. The chart shows the characteristic curves for each of the chemical compounds, on the basis of which the chemist can determine the structural formula.

Another instrument is the polarimeter, which passes a beam of polarized light (light that vibrates in only one plane) through the sample. The emerging beam has a different plane of polarization; and the difference, which is measured, gives information about the composition of the sample. Then there is the refractometer, which measures the refractive index or light-bending power, which is different for each compound—and thus serves as another method of identification.

Still another technique used by the analytical chemist is chromatography. The mixture in solution is placed on special paper, which hangs down vertically. In a given time, one chemical component will travel further down the paper than another. When the paper is treated with a dye, the individual compounds show up at different levels. By means of their positions, relative to those of *known* substances, the chemist can determine the composition of each component in the mixture.

Since no one instrument can give all the information required, the analytical chemist has need of all of them. Thus one test may indicate that a compound belongs to a particular group, but another test may fail to show the presence of certain properties that are characteristic of this group. Is this due to impurities or are other factors involved? In an attempt to answer this question, the chemist must use not only book-knowledge but also his imagination, based on experience.

Other machines in his laboratory make use of X rays for analysis. Consider the problem: How much quartz does a sample of dust contain? This is an important health problem because the inhalation of quartz dust may result in a serious lung disease called silicosis which is common among miners. The old methods of analysis are in many cases undependable and have been superseded by the X-ray diffraction technique. This technique is based on the fact that each type of mineral has a characteristic powder diffraction pattern produced by the X rays. The mineral can thus be identified by its particular pattern. X-ray diffraction is sensitive enough to differentiate between two types of titanium oxide, a white pigment. It is difficult to distinguish one type from the other by routine chemical analysis.

A more recently developed analyzer, the Van de Graaf accelerator, converts elements into radioactive isotopes by irradiating them with a neutron beam. The elements are identified by their characteristic radiation pattern. In this case the chemical composition is determined by nuclear rather than by electronic or chemical properties, an example of the overlapping of physics and chemistry.

In large chemical plants conventional techniques in analytical chemistry are yielding in part to automation. Take the Autoanalyzer; its operation is completely automatic. The samples to be analyzed are picked up, pumped along, and mixed with a flowing, diluting stream. The diluted sample passes through an apparatus that automatically separates its components, which are then fed into a reagent stream. The stream flows through a variety of instruments which analyze the components, and the findings are automatically recorded on a moving graph.

The new analyzing techniques are used in the food industry to measure and analyze the appearance, taste, and odor of foods. Color filters, combined with sensitive phototubes, inspect vegetables, and photoelectric cells inspect and control the color of beer. Electronic instruments determine the texture, form, and size of food; methods have even been developed to analyze the taste factor. For example, the degree of sweetness can be measured by the refractometer which determines the refractive index, since this index changes in accordance with the concentration of sugar present. The degree of bitterness is measured by "taste panels"; the amount of salt (salinity), by conductivity measurements. Analytical chemists are even trying to measure and classify odors by isolating the odor components in food materials.

All these analytical machines, miraculous though they seem, will probably appear primitive by the standards of 1980. Foreshadowing what is to come is the new electronic spectroanalyzer. It can identify and measure simultaneously as many as ten components in a sample, including any organic mixture, and it does so in a matter of minutes instead of the usual period of days or weeks. The machine includes a recording device and a high-speed digital computer to perform the calculations and record the analytical findings.

The analytical chemist in former years was concerned only with chemical properties and reactions; today he is interested also in physical properties and their measurements, including the refractive index, fluorescence, viscosity and vapor pressure. By the methods of stereochemistry, he can determine the exact positions in different planes of the atoms in an organic compound. So many techniques have been borrowed from the arsenal of the physicist that a new term, "analytical physics," has been coined, meaning the use of physical methods for chemical analysis.

Apart from the contributions of the physicist, it was the development and expansion of organic chemistry that was responsible for making analytical chemistry the broad and complex science that it is today. Until the first decades of the century, the chemical world was dominated by inorganic chemicals. This type of chemical could be analyzed efficiently, for the most part, by the classical methods of qualitative and quantitative analysis. Organic compounds, on the other hand, are much more complex, both in composition and in structure, with possibly hundreds of atoms linked together in different planes. It was the need to analyze these compounds that led to revolutionary new methods.

The analytical chemist may also serve as a consultant. Engineers of all kinds, in different industries, may turn to him for help in solving problems that involve materials. He may discover that the solution has nothing to do with chemical factors; or that the answer can be found in standard tables or in the chemical literature; or that an organic chemist should be consulted. If the job involves this kind of consultative work, the analytical chemist should have a considerable knowledge of industrial materials and processes and also of economic costs.[3]

Contrary to the impression held by many people, the work of the industrial analytical chemist is far from routine. New products that require new and improved methods of analysis are being continually developed. He must answer such questions as the following: Will a particular material be stable under given conditions of temperature, pressure, friction? If not, what can be done to ensure its stability? In determining the structure of unknown compounds, he may discover valuable new compounds, making him an important factor in the development of new products.

Yesterday a routine laboratory technician, today the analytical chemist is a scientist who must exercise keen judgment in the solution of complex problems. Unlike the technician who merely follows cut-and-dried instructions, his role is "to ascertain that the instructions are correct and are properly carried out." [4]

In addition to his other duties, the analytical chemist in industry is frequently called upon by the sales and marketing departments of his company to help solve a customer's technical problems. It may be that the customer cannot make the complicated analyses that may be required, owing to his limited laboratory facilities. The chemist may have to devise simplified methods of analysis. He may have to determine the cause of corrosion in containers filled with chemicals, or of undesirable reactions between a container and its contents. Everyone depends on him for information which they cannot get elsewhere, including research chemists; chemists concerned with the control of processes; marketing authorities faced with problems of contamination and of meeting purity specifications. Even the legal department of a company may ask his advice regarding the proper characterization of chemicals, when applying for a patent. The analytical chemist also bears the responsibility for making sure that his company's products meet the quality specifications of the Food and Drug Administration.

We have said enough to suggest that the traits and qualifications discussed in Chapter Three apply also to the analytical chemist. However, if he is employed in an industrial plant he must also have the capacity to work fast and accurately under pressure. He may receive a dozen rush orders for analyses of samples at the same time, and must quickly decide which of them should have priority. This can be a delicate problem, involving diplomatic as well as technical and economic considerations. Jobs may pile up fast in an industrial laboratory, and the chemist must be able to plan and organize his work efficiently.

If you wish to be an industrial analytical chemist, therefore, you must decide beforehand whether you are willing, and have the capacity, to work under the high-pressure conditions that prevail in some plants. It may be that you are temperamentally fitted for a calmer, more leisurely, atmosphere, in which case you will be happier in nonindustrial or academic work, especially if you have a bent for basic, rather than applied, research. Some companies offer opportunities for fundamental research in analytical chemistry, but the majority are interested only in practical applications or in obtaining data or findings needed for projects that are currently in operation.

In spite of the pressure, many chemists prefer working in the industrial field because of its varied activities and stimulating problems. Their contacts with top executives, as well as with the heads of production and research departments, give them unusual opportunities for recognition. To those who are qualified, a career in this field is a challenging one, in addition to being remunerative. Though the industrial analytical chemist does not have as much opportunity for basic research as he would have in a university, he is encouraged to work on various research projects, the reports of which are frequently published in chemical and chemical engineering journals. In fact 45 per cent of all research papers published by analytical chemists were found, in a 1949 study, to have been written by industrial chemists.[5]

An interesting division of chemistry is microchemistry, which is concerned with analyses of minute traces of materials. As a microchemist, you would work in a "micro" laboratory, using miniature retorts, one-inch test tubes and one-inch porcelain containers instead of the conventional-sized crucibles. Your weighing machine would be a microbalance which can weigh accurately to one ten-millionth of an ounce.

This seems fantastically accurate but, in Al Jolson's words, you ain't heard nothin' yet! More recently, ultramicrochemistry—a thousand times more refined as a method of investigation than microchemistry—was developed. It measures to a millionth of a *gram* (a gram is about the weight of a fly)! Ultramicrochemistry has important applications in many areas, notably in biochemistry. (For example, it enables the chemist to determine exactly where an insecticide accumulates in the body of an insect.)

Analytical chemists have advanced far since the day when they were mere laboratory technicians. The words of Beverly L. Clarke, written in 1937, are even more true today than they were then: "The skillful analyst deserves a status parallel with that of other research workers; for the proper performance of any save the most perfunctory of analytical procedures, requires an alertness and originality comparable to that required elsewhere in research. . . . Advances in the field of analytical chemistry in the past decade or so have been nothing short of phenomenal, but few outside the profession are at all aware of this progress." [6]

CHAPTER SEVEN

The Biochemist

THE BIOCHEMIST IS CONCERNED WITH THE CHEMISTRY OF living matter, both animal and vegetable. Like the organic chemist, he deals with organic—and therefore with carbon —compounds. However, his particular field of study is concerned with the effects of chemicals on living organisms; the chemical changes that go on inside the body, under different conditions; the manner in which compounds are "metabolized" (utilized) in the tissue of plants or animals. As authorities have stated: "The ultimate goal of biochemistry is to describe the phenomena that distinguish the 'living' from the 'non-living' in the language of chemistry and physics."[1]

The work of the biochemist may overlap that of chemists in other fields. He may find it necessary to make a chemical analysis, like the analytical chemist, or purify chemicals, like the organic chemist. To give one example: two biochemists of the School of Medicine at Western Reserve University were recently faced with the problem of removing from a vitamin chemical impurities that they suspected were responsible for certain effects on enzymes. In order to do so, they found that they had to develop a new method of purifying the vitamin, and finally succeeded in perfecting such a method. Biochemists may also synthesize compounds, though this is generally limited to substances like proteins or insulin that are present in the living body.

Biochemistry as a career comprises a broad spectrum of activities that merges, on one end, into organic chemistry and, on the other end, into biology and medicine. A biochemist may specialize in particular fields like chemotherapy (the treatment of diseases by chemicals) or the study of enzymes. In the course of his work, he may isolate antibiotics from molds, inject chemicals into living bodies, or dissect the bodies to study the effects of the chemicals.

Many biochemists are employed in medical schools where they teach or do research, for biochemistry is closely related to medicine. One of the first to demonstrate this relationship, as noted in an earlier chapter, was Paracelsus (1493–1541). It was not until the eighteenth century, however, that the scientific foundations of biochemistry were laid, thanks chiefly to the epoch-making experiments of Lavoisier, who was the first to demonstrate that respiration has a chemical basis. ("Respiration," he wrote in 1780, "is therefore a combustion—slow, it is true, but otherwise perfectly similar to that of charcoal.") In the nineteenth century Emil Fischer succeeded in breaking complex living tissue down into simpler chemical compounds for the first time. In addition, an increasing number of organic compounds were derived from living cells. Many other discoveries were made, and the science of biochemistry expanded rapidly. Today biochemists are recognized as among the most important scientists working in the field of medical research.*

---

* Two American biochemists, Dr. Severo Ochoa and Dr. Arthur Kornberg, shared the Nobel Prize in Medicine in 1959. The award was for their discoveries regarding the biological synthesis of certain complex organic compounds in the body.

One reason for this recognition is the important role they have played in the development of drugs and antibiotics. The story of antibiotics begins with a question mark in the brain of that great chemist Louis Pasteur. Why, Pasteur wondered, do disease germs disappear soon after they are buried in the soil? Is it possible, he speculated, that they are destroyed by other microbes that live in the earth? Pasteur's hunch turned out to be correct, but this was not definitely established until 1928 when Dr. Alexander Fleming, English bacteriologist, accidentally discovered penicillin, the first effective antibiotic.

Dr. Fleming had grown a colony of staphylococcus germs on a saucerlike dish in his laboratory. One day he noticed that the culture had been contaminated by a blue-green mold, a spore of which had drifted through an open window and settled on the dish. He discovered, to his surprise, that many of the germs had been destroyed, apparently by a chemical ingredient of the mold. Later, he extracted this ingredient and named it penicillin. With this drug he succeeded in clearing up an infection in a laboratory mouse. This was exciting news, but the public report of his discovery aroused little interest at the time. In 1939 Dr. Ernst Chain, a biochemist, and Dr. Howard W. Florey, a pathologist, developed a mold similar to Dr. Fleming's, and injected the penicillin into sick human beings for the first time. The results were so successful that a large research program was instituted with the object of developing satisfactory methods of mass production of the drug. Almost $30,000,000 was spent on this project before it succeeded. In the vast penicillin-making plants of today, the liquid-culture medium in which the molds are grown fills vats almost two stories high. The penicillin is derived from the molds by a complicated process of fermentation. Mass production has lowered the price of penicillin from $35.00 for

100,000 units, to $0.20. The drug is credited with having saved countless lives during the Second World War by making possible the successful treatment of wounds and infections that would otherwise have been fatal, and has since become one of the indispensable drugs of modern medicine.

The success of penicillin spurred research for other molds and antibiotics. In 1944 Dr. Selman A. Waksman, of Rutgers University, and his associates, discovered streptomycin; a few years later, aureomycin was isolated from molds taken from the soil of a barnyard in Missouri. In 1949 terramycin, one of the most powerful of all antibiotics, was discovered. Significantly, it required only ten months for this drug to be accepted—in contrast to the fifteen years that intervened from the time penicillin was discovered and developed experimentally to the time the medical profession began prescribing it.

As a biochemist working in the field of antibiotics, your work would consist of isolating the drugs from their molds, administering them to laboratory animals, and studying the effects on the animals' metabolism. Working jointly with microbiologists, you would determine whether or not a new mold was worth cultivating, judging by its potential yield of antibiotics. You would have to be thoroughly familiar with the various strains of molds and the effectiveness of each type of antibiotic in combating specific diseases. You might discover new applications for these drugs. It has recently been reported that molds are being investigated as a possible source of antibiotics that destroy cancer cells. Dr. Paul Burkholder, the microbiologist who discovered chloromycetin, is directing a research program which has already involved the examination of more than 100,000 molds for this purpose. In laboratory tests, living cancer cells have been destroyed by some of these anti-biotics.

Biochemists are active in other fields of cancer research as well. In a report of research work done at the Sloan-Kettering Institute, Alfred P. Sloan said in 1957: "Chemo-therapy is our best hope for more effective cancer control in the future." The report stated that cancer cells in animals had been destroyed by chemicals which also seemed to re-lieve human victims of cancer. A chemical compound called properdin apparently builds up immunity to the disease. Laboratory tests have shown that when small doses of a yeast product are fed to animals, it seems to make them less susceptible to cancer by increasing the amount of properdin in the body.

Recognition of the importance of biochemistry in this field was reflected in the appointment in 1958 of Dr. Julius Schultz, a biochemist, as director of the new cancer re-search institute at Hahnemann's Medical College in Phila-delphia—one of the few cancer institutes in the country headed by a biochemist. Dr. Schultz, who got his Ph.D. degree in biochemistry at Michigan University, had previ-ously been an assistant professor at Temple University Medical School.

Scientists claim that before we can have a basic under-standing of the cause of cancer, we must know more about the metabolism of the normal living cell, since cancer causes an abnormal growth of cells. In this field, also, biochemists have scored important advances. Complete chemical analy-sis of the contents of a single living cell is impossible at present, for various reasons, but biochemists have overcome this handicap by means of an ingenious technique. Hun-dreds of cells are homogenized in a single mass in a centri-fuge, which whirls the mass around at different rates of speed. At low velocity, the nuclei of the cells drop out, followed, as the speed increases, by the smaller elements. By analyzing a large group of nuclei obtained in this manner, biochemists can make a chemical analysis of them and thus obtain information about the nucleus of the individual cell.

Important discoveries have been made as a result of this method. Consider the rod-shaped chromosomes in the nucleus of the cell. They contain the genes that transmit characteristics from parent to offspring. These chromosomes consist largely of chemical units called nucleotides, which are linked together in long, chainlike molecules. Incredibly small though these chemicals are, biochemists were able to discover that their surfaces are dotted with phosphorus compounds having a negative electrical charge. Recently, V. G. Allfrey and A. E. Mirsky, two biochemists of the Rockefeller Institute in New York, removed these nucleotides in experiments and discovered that this resulted in a loss of energy by the nucleus and an impairment of its ability to manufacture proteins. By substituting other, negatively charged compounds for the nucleotides, they restored the energy of the nucleus. The substitution of a compound with a positive charge, however, slowed down the activity of the nucleus.

This discovery must have been an exciting one to these biochemists, because it has tremendous implications. The cell nucleus normally contains positively charged compounds called histones, which seem to retard the activity of the nucleus. Question: Is the function of the histones to act as a control, to prevent overactivity of the nucleus and so preserve the proper balance? The answer to this question has a vital bearing on the metabolism of the normal living cell. In addition, it suggests a possible method of controlling cancer, since cancer is an overactivity of cells. If positive electrical charges inhibit the growth of cells, as these experiments suggest, perhaps positively charged compounds like histones may inhibit or even prevent cancer.

In their studies of living cells, biochemists have also investigated the cytoplasm—the jellylike substance that fills the interior of the cell and surrounds the nucleus. This jelly contains minute "islands" that are 1/50,000th of an inch in diameter. The membranes of these "islands" burn oxygen and transform food into energy. Biochemists are studying the chemical changes involved in these reactions, which are the sources of energy needed to make the muscles of the body contract and to transmit nerve impulses. They are trying to take this submicroscopic power plant apart and determine the structure of its constituents. Their findings may throw further light on the cause of cancer, since some authorities believe that it may be produced by the inability of some cells to "breathe" and burn oxygen properly.

As a biochemist, you might study amines, a group of chemicals which play an important role in the proper functioning of the brain and nervous system and which keep the blood pressure at normal levels. Amines are produced by enzymes (living catalysts). When there are too many amines in the body, the excess is eliminated by other enzymes which destroy them and thus may cause an increase in the blood pressure. Chemists have developed drugs that attack the amine-destroying enzymes. These drugs may therefore prove to be effective in reducing high blood pressure without the undesirable effects caused by other drugs used at present. Amines also check epilepsy. Biochemists have developed a drug that increases the amount of amines in the brain and therefore tends to inhibit epileptic convulsions.

They have also scored important advances in our knowledge of hormones. In 1935 Dr. Edward C. Kendall, a biochemist of the Mayo Clinic, isolated cortisone, a hormone secreted by the adrenal glands. Cortisone proved to be a miracle drug that has saved the lives of countless people suffering from arthritis. Crystallized from chemical compounds in the bile of oxen, it was at first beyond the reach of all but the wealthy. Later, a new source of cortisone was discovered in the root of a Mexican plant called barbasco. This is the chief commercial source used today. Cortisone is still a relatively expensive drug, but it costs far less than the $4,000 per ounce that one had to pay for it when it was first derived from the bile of oxen!

Many other hormones have been isolated by biochemists —including the famous ACTH. Some medical authorities believe that the full potential of hormones as a curative agency is still to be realized and that hormones may prove to be the key to the origin of cancer and mental diseases.

Another field in which biochemists have made notable gains in recent years is that of proteins. When the protein insulin was isolated in 1922, and used to combat diabetes, the achievement was hailed as one of the most important contributions to modern medicine. Like all proteins, insulin is an enormously complicated compound, consisting of fifty-one amino-acid units, which are the building blocks of the protein. These are strung together in long, folded chains. Owing to insulin's complicated structure, biochemists were baffled until recently in their attempts to determine its exact composition. The task was finally accomplished by Dr. Frederick Sanger, a British biochemist, after ten years of experimentation. For this brilliant feat he was awarded the Nobel Prize in 1958.

When Dr. Sanger began his investigation, the relative position of each amino-acid unit in the structural chains was not known. Dr. Sanger solved the problem by breaking up an insulin molecule into fragments and then applying a chemical that stained yellow only those units occupying

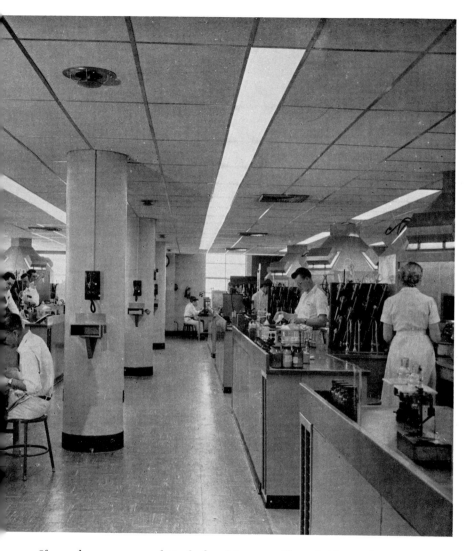

If you become an analytical chemist, you will probably work in a laboratory similar to this one. Clean and orderly in appearance, it is equipped with the latest and most scientific instruments for precise chemical analysis. *(Courtesy Monsanto Chemical Company)*

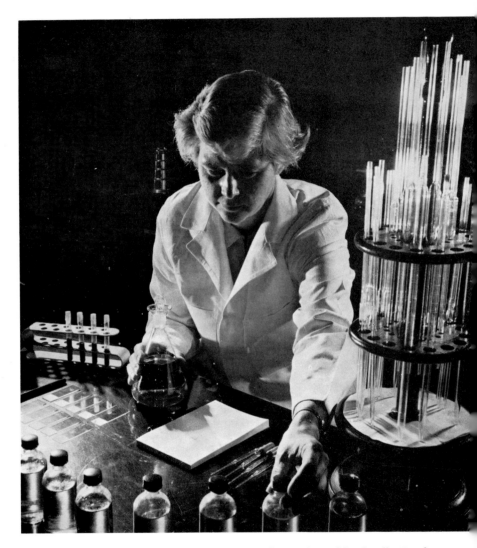

Biochemist studying the effects of chemicals on blood cells. Biochemists subject new compounds to elaborate and exhaustive tests before they are permitted to be sold commercially. (*Courtesy E. I. du Pont de Nemours and Company, Inc.*)

end positions in each fragment. With infinite patience, he reassembled the fragments into the original chain pattern, much as one puts together the parts of a complicated jigsaw puzzle. The relative position of each of the fifty-one units in the chains was thus definitely established.

Now that we know its structure, can we look forward to the commercial production of synthetic insulin? This is a formidable task that may take years to accomplish; yet, in view of the amazing chemical achievements in recent years, it would be rash to say that it will never be done.

Scientists are advancing rapidly in their knowledge of proteins. Some ten years ago, two biochemists from the University of California succeeded after fifteen years of experiments in determining the structure of the protein molecules that make up hair or fur. They discovered that the molecules were linked together in seven-strand cables. More recently, another protein—a hormone produced by the pituitary gland—was synthesized by the biochemist Klaus Hoffman and his associates. It is the largest protein molecule that has yet been created in a test tube, consisting of a chain of thirteen amino-acid molecules.

Biochemists have also made valuable contributions in the treatment of mental illness by drugs, as well as in establishing a chemical basis for mental disorders. Drugs like reserpine have had an amazing success in sharply reducing the number of patients that had to be admitted to mental hospitals, though it is not yet understood why the drug has such a tranquilizing effect on the patient. A possible explanation was provided recently, when biochemists and medical scientists discovered that reserpine releases a compound called serotonin from the central nervous system. This compound is present in the brain and helps to control its functioning.

The idea that emotional and mental disturbances have a biochemical rather than a psychological basis has been gaining ground among scientists in recent years. A distinguished adherent of this concept is Dr. Daniel Bovet, a Swiss-born biochemist, who in 1957 received the Nobel Prize in physiology and medicine. He and his wife, who assists him in research, are at present engaged in studying the chemistry of the human brain, especially as it is affected by mental illness and by drugs. Bovet believes that mental disorders are caused by chemical imbalance in the body.

In 1958 Dr. William Malamud reported to the National Association for Mental Health that thanks largely to biochemical research, a breakthrough was imminent in the treatment of schizophrenia, a serious mental disease that has so far resisted all treatment.[2] The symptoms of schizophrenia have been artificially induced in human volunteers by the injection of drugs, and then markedly reduced by means of chemical compounds. Some biochemists believe that the apathy and lack of energy shown by schizophrenics are caused by a deficiency of phosphorus, thus opening up another path of investigation.

Another distinguished chemist who is engaged in the study of the chemical aspects of mental diseases is Dr. Linus C. Pauling, winner of the 1954 Nobel Prize in chemistry. Dr. Pauling believes that many diseases may be caused by the abnormal structure of chemicals either in the genes or in the body itself; these he calls "molecular diseases." Dr. Pauling said, "I foresee the day when many of these diseases will be treated by means of artificial enzymes." He has predicted that someday doctors will be able to insert a tube with an open end containing a catalyst into the artery of the newborn child who has inherited a mental disease and that this catalyst will prevent the disease.

Biochemists seek to combat pain as well as mental illness. Recently reported is the discovery of a new pain-killing drug, called NIH 7519, that is ten times as effective as morphine. It was discovered by Dr. Everett L. May, biochemist, in cooperation with Dr. Nathan B. Eddy, medical scientist. They developed the drug from that amazing, ubiquitous source of dyes and pharmaceuticals: coal tar. NIH 7519 is very expensive at present because of difficulties in manufacturing, but efforts are being made to bring its price within the reach of sick people in underdeveloped areas. Dr. Arthur S. Flemming, United States Secretary of Health, Education and Welfare, who reported the results of preliminary tests of this drug, referred to the discovery as "an exciting breakthrough."

We have stressed the research contributions of biochemists because of their great scientific importance. However, biochemists are also needed in private industry to investigate the biological effects of various commercial products. For example, they may study the reactions of the skin to soaps and cosmetics in order to evaluate their effectiveness and determine whether they have any toxic qualities. "Product evaluation," as this kind of analysis and testing is called, is an important part of the work of the industrial biochemist, who plays a basic role in helping to decide whether or not the countless chemical consumer products developed in laboratories are suitable and safe for commercial use.

The Clinical Chemist

An interesting offshoot of biochemistry in the medical field is *clinical chemistry*. The clinical chemist is generally employed in a hospital laboratory where he makes chemical analyses of blood, urine, and so on, as well as various biochemical tests.

Fifty years ago, the clinical chemist was little more than a hospital laboratory technician who performed routine analytical tests. According to the American Association of Clinical Chemists, the clinical chemist of today is trained to make as many as one hundred different kinds of tests and analyses. He is qualified also to supervise the laboratory and assist the medical staff of the hospital in the interpretation of findings. Some clinical chemists even do research work at universities or medical schools in projects supported by the United States Public Health Institute or the American Heart and Cancer Associations.

To become a clinical chemist, you must take graduate courses—after receiving your B.S. degree in chemistry—in such medical subjects as physiology, as well as in biochemistry and advanced chemistry. Most clinical chemists have a Ph.D. degree. The association recommends, in addition, a year of internship in the analytical laboratory of a large, well-equipped hospital, for basic training and experience.

Relatively few students are able or willing to pursue such a long and arduous course of training. The association itself admits that only about three hundred chemists in the entire country are sufficiently qualified to meet its rigorous standards. Yet there is a definite and steady demand for the services of clinical chemists, and at least a thousand are needed in hospitals alone. They are employed also in universities and in medical schools, and a small number in private industry.

Most clinical chemists are relatively well paid. A survey in 1954 of seventeen clinical chemists (of whom all but two had Ph.D. degrees) showed that their average income ranged from $8,000 to $10,500 a year.

The Agricultural Biochemist

In the chapter on organic chemistry, we referred to the contributions of chemists to agriculture. In this field particularly, the work of the organic chemist overlaps that of the biochemist, and one cannot draw a sharp occupational line between the two specialties. Even the organic agricultural chemist must have some knowledge of the chemistry of plant life which is the special domain of the biochemist. There are, however, areas that are definitely within one specialty or the other. Chemurgy, for example—the transformation of farm products into industrial materials—is in the field of the organic chemist, just as an investigation of the effects of antibiotics on the growth and behavior of livestock would fall in the domain of the biochemist.

A recent contribution of the biochemist to agriculture is the use of chemicals to make plants resistant to heat. One of these chemicals is riboflavin, a component of the vitamin B complex, of which only a fraction of an ounce is needed for the purpose. Discussing the importance of biochemical studies in this field, Dr. Edwin B. Kurtz, Jr., of the University of Arizona College of Agriculture, writes: "A knowledge of how desert plants tolerate high temperatures—and the use of this information for the chemical cure of climatic ills of economic plants—will help solve the critical food problem of the world by permitting agriculture to extend into new lands and by increasing the yield of presently cultivated areas." He adds that a chemical explanation of the damage to plants caused by heat "offers a new and fascinating avenue of exploration." [3]

As an agricultural chemist, you might study the biological effects of chemical fungicides. Not long ago the staff of biochemists at du Pont's Haskell Laboratory for Toxicology and Industrial Medicine was assigned the task of determining whether or not spraying tomato crops with a new fungicide presented a health hazard to consumers. The biochemists fed lethal doses of the chemical to white rats (whose reactions resemble those of humans). Working with pathologists, they analyzed blood samples taken from the tails of the rats and examined various tissue specimens under the microscope to determine whether the chemical had had any effect on body organs. Not until the fungicide was found to be completely safe, even when traces of it remained in the tomatoes sold to the consumer, was it placed on the market. It had taken nine years of research and field testing for the fungicide to pass from the research laboratory to the tomato grower. This is only one of scores of projects in which biochemists are employed to ensure the safety of chemicals used in the growth and processing of food.

Many biochemists specialize in a study of the chemistry of plant life. Radioisotopes (elements made radioactive in atomic energy plants) constitute an important new research tool that helps these biochemists solve the mysteries of biological processes. Consider photosynthesis, the process by which plants convert carbon dioxide and water into starch and cellulose with the aid of sunlight. Perhaps someday we shall be able to duplicate this vastly intricate process and, like nature, create foodstuffs out of chemicals. To investigate photosynthesis, biochemists send radioactive carbon and hydrogen atoms into plant cells. Geiger counters trace these atoms through various chemical reactions, giving biochemists information regarding the various stages of the process. Radioisotope "tracers," to be discussed in a later chapter, are also used to determine what chemicals are necessary for the diet of livestock to keep them productive.

Biochemists make use of radioactivity to change the inherited characteristics of plants and produce new varieties. In "atomic farms" concentric rows of plants are grown around a powerful radioactive source. This source produces remarkable changes in the plants, including the creation of a new strain of oats that is resistant to blight. Biochemists, studying the chemical effects of this radiation, are delving deep into the secrets of the chemistry of plant life.

Recently the importance of chemicals in improving the quality of meat was dramatically demonstrated when, at a luncheon held in New York, thirty-four editors sampled two kinds of steak. One kind had been cut from steers that had been injected with a tranquilizing drug; the other kind of steak was from untreated steers. The meat that was favored by a three-to-one vote turned out to be from tranquilized animals. The drug used in the experiment is manufactured by a company in Kansas City, Missouri, of which Dr. Vladimir Dvorkovitz, a biochemist, is president. He explained that when the drug was injected into the stomachs of steers at the ranch, it had the effect of quieting animals which would otherwise go off their feed, because of fears of various origins, and lose weight in consequence. He added, "We can improve the quality of all meat this way and save the livestock industry $100,000,000 a year by cutting losses and handling costs." [4]

The Food Chemist

A more specialized offshoot of biochemistry is food chemistry. The food chemist is concerned with the chemical composition of foods, their nutritional value, their proper preservation, their improvement by means of chemical additives, and the relationship of food intake to metabolism.

The food requirements of the body have been thoroughly

investigated, and much knowledge has accumulated on the subject. We now know that some sixty different chemical substances are needed to support human life at peak efficiency. To the basic ingredients of proteins, fats, and carbohydrates, nature, the supreme biochemist, has added certain chemicals to make the food colorful, edible, and tasty. Chemists can synthesize some of these foods in the laboratory by duplicating their chemical constituents, and their findings in these experiments have given us a deeper understanding of nutritional requirements.

Following the lead of nature, food chemists furnish chemical additives to make food tastier, more desirable and nutritious. Calcium salts, for example, added to canned tomatoes, keep them firm and fresh looking. Glycerine enables food to retain its moisture and improves its flavor. Small quantities of iodine, added to table salt, help prevent thyroid deficiency; and the addition of synthetic vitamin D to milk prevents rickets in children.

The food chemist also develops chemicals that preserve food and protect it against the ravages of pests in granaries and against contamination by bacteria. Without this method of preservation, there would be enormous losses of food products with a consequent great increase in prices. In food-processing plants, chemicals are used as detergents in the washing of produce, and chemical wrappings protect the food from bacteria and fungi.

It is obvious that food chemists play a most important part in the protection of public health. Synthetic chemical additives have sharply reduced the number of deaths and diseases that are caused by improper or inadequate diet. Chemists have supplied the necessary vitamins, minerals, and amino acids that may be lacking in food or not present in sufficient quantities.

The importance of synthetic vitamins was dramatically

demonstrated in 1948 on the Bataan Peninsula, where the chief food of the natives is polished rice from which the part containing vitamins has been removed. As a result of this diet, many thousands suffered from beriberi, a vitamin-deficiency disease. When synthetic vitamins were added to the diet, the number of deaths from beriberi decreased by over 67 per cent—yet the vitamin-additive cost only thirty-five cents per person for an entire year!

In the United States chemical enrichment of flour, corn meal, and bread has almost abolished pellagra, another vitamin-deficiency disease, in Southern states, where it was once very prevalent—another triumph for the food chemist. In recent years sodium fluoride has been added to drinking-water reservoirs in many communities in an effort to prevent tooth decay. Thanks to the contributions of the chemist, nearly every adult American now eats food that he rarely saw on his table when he was a child; and since the last world war new kinds of processed foods—canned, frozen, or dehydrated—have been developed.

As a food chemist, you would be employed in the chemical or food industry or by a government agency like the Food and Drug Administration. Your work would be in analyzing and testing chemical additives and foodstuffs. On the other hand, you might do basic research in nutrition. As in other fields of biochemistry, there is no sharp line of demarcation between the research work of the food chemist and that of the biologist or medical scientist, for the food chemist must understand the processes of digestion and assimilation as well as the chemical composition of foods. Opportunities for research in this field are excellent. Many research projects are supported by the food industry. Since 1942 they have spent more than $4,000,000 for this purpose.

We have said enough to indicate the vast scope of biochemistry. It offers a fascinating career, but one that requires extensive and rigorous training and education. If you desire to become a biochemist after receiving your B.S. in chemistry, you will have to take graduate courses in subjects such as colloids and electrochemistry, as well as biological or medical courses pertaining to your specialized field of work. For example, if you plan to specialize in the medical field, you will take such courses as physiology, histology (microscopic anatomy), pharmacology, and bacteriology. For specialization in the biochemistry of plant life, on the other hand, you will study plant biology, fungi, cytology (cell life), and algae or mosses. If you do graduate work at a research center like the Agricultural Experiment Station at the University of Arizona, you will study the metabolism of plant life or investigate the chemistry of nutrition in animals or the toxic effects of certain insects on livestock.

The field of research in biochemistry as a whole is exceptionally broad. It embraces medicine, botany, genetics, entomology (insect study), and even aspects of space travel, as indicated by a recent report by an Air Force biochemist in which he revealed that new strains of infectious bacteria are present in space, presenting a health hazard to future space travelers!

The income of biochemists is not generally as high as that of industrial chemists, which may be one reason why only about 6 per cent of all chemists specialize in this field. Nevertheless, biochemistry will always attract young people who are interested in biology or medicine as well as in chemistry. Its research aspects will interest those whose prime purpose in studying chemistry is to seek answers to the fundamental questions that have fascinated philosophers and scientists in all ages: "What is biologic life? How does it function and how does the individual transmit charac-

teristics to his offspring?" Just as the atomic physicist probes
the secrets of nature in the atoms of inanimate matter, the
biochemist does the same in the living tissues of plants and
animals.

CHAPTER EIGHT

Physical Chemistry and Other Fields of Chemistry

IN THE EARLY NINETEENTH CENTURY THE LINE OF DEMARCA-
tion between chemistry and physics was sharply defined;
today it is blurred. In some areas of chemical knowledge,
it is difficult to say where chemistry ends and physics begins.
Increasingly, as we have seen, the chemist has borrowed
instruments from the rich tool chest of the physicist, for
both analysis and research. *Chemical Abstracts* is read by
physicists as well as by chemists; about 75 per cent of all
papers published in various journals of physics are abstracted
in this chemical publication.

In that branch of chemistry called *physical chemistry,*
the two sciences fuse. The physical chemist applies mathematics and concepts of physics to his studies of the chemical behavior of solids, liquids, and gases. He measures
various physical properties, such as heat-resistance, brittle-
ness, density, vapor pressure. He analyzes mathematically
processes like absorption, adsorption, and diffusion; he in-
vestigates the effects of light, electricity, radioactivity, and
other radiations on chemical reactions. He also studies the
structures of molecules of substances by spectroscopy and

calculates the changes in structure necessary to produce various desired properties.

Two basic studies in which the physical chemist must be thoroughly grounded are thermodynamics and kinetics. Thermodynamics deals with the mechanical effects of heat, under various conditions, on solids, liquids, and gases. It is involved in practically all chemical reactions. In the Haber process, for example, ammonia is manufactured by combining nitrogen with hydrogen under certain temperatures and pressures. If these change beyond a certain point, the process is reversed and the ammonia is broken down again into nitrogen and hydrogen. Thermodynamics enables the physical chemist to calculate the temperatures and pressures necessary to keep the process going in one direction.

Chemical kinetics, another basic study, is concerned with the time element, the rate of reaction or the reaction time of chemical processes. How long does it take chemicals to react in order to obtain the highest yield? This question is of great importance in the chemical industry, and the answer is supplied by means of chemical kinetics on the basis of the temperature, pressure, type of catalyst used, and other factors. More heat usually means faster production, but it may result in a lower yield. Kinetics enables the chemist to calculate the temperatures needed to give a sufficiently high yield at a reasonable rate of speed. It is used also in studies of the conduction of electricity through gases, in studies of adsorption, and in many other investigations.

The methods used in physical chemistry apply as much to research in biology and medicine as they do to research in chemistry. They are used in studying the structure of proteins as well as of plastics. Indeed, physical chemists are responsible for many advances in the biological sciences and their methods have been incorporated into the techniques of biological experimentation.[1]

Apparently simple chemical phenomena are often the result of complicated processes. Consider the simple act of putting salt in a glass of water and then stirring it with a spoon. Why does the salt dissolve and why does it dissolve faster when you stir it more vigorously? The reasons were not clearly understood until theories of solutions and of diffusion were developed. We now know that when a salt dissolves, the sodium and chloride ions (electrically charged particles) of which it consists separate from each other. The laws of diffusion, formulated in the first decade of this century, enable the chemist to calculate the movement of these ions in solution. The magnitude of the reactions involved is indicated by the fact that a single drop of water contains 168.3 million, million, million molecules!

Charcoal is frequently used to remove coloring matter from solutions. Here is another apparently simple phenomenon; yet it is so complicated that it was not fully explained until 1916 when Dr. Irving Langmuir proposed his theory of adsorption, as this process is called. The theory explains the manner in which a certain proportion of the molecules in solution adhere to the surface of the charcoal while the remaining molecules go back into solution. Adsorption is useful for many purposes. For example, adsorbing materials accelerate chemical reactions, fix dyes on materials and, in the form of charcoal, adsorb chlorine gas in gas masks.

Physical chemists have also added to our knowledge of the structure of atoms and molecules through the medium of spectroscopy. It had been shown by Rutherford and Bohr that different atoms contain different quantities of energy. (More precisely their electrons occupy different "energy levels" within the atom.) When an atom absorbs or emits radiations, the energy jumps from one level to another—

and this is true also of molecules. When chemical compounds are irradiated in a spectroscope, the absorption of the radiant energy raises the energy level of the compound. The amount, which is calculated, reveals the energy level of the particular atom. Physical chemists use special techniques in these spectroscopic investigations. As in the case of so many other techniques that were developed solely to increase our fundamental knowledge, these proved to have practical applications as well. With the use of infrared, visible, and ultraviolet rays, the physical chemist can detect impurities in materials; he can also determine the chemical composition of mixtures that cannot be ascertained by ordinary chemical analysis.

An interesting field of activity of physical chemists is the modification of the properties of materials by alteration of their molecular structure. This is accomplished in various ways. In the case of polyethylene, a well known plastic, for example, the desired properties can be obtained by selecting either the high-pressure or the low-pressure method of manufacture. By analyzing the effects of these different pressures, the physical chemist can determine the properties in advance. Similar effects can be produced also by the electron-beam generator, which emits electrons from the heated filament of a cathode, as in a vacuum tube. The electrons, accelerated by high-voltage electrodes, travel with a speed approaching that of light, and collide with electrons in the molecules, making the plastic tougher and more resistant to high temperatures, acids, and detergents. Electron-beam irradiation has many other uses. It can vulcanize rubber and can convert petroleum hydrocarbons into high-octane gasoline without the need for catalysts. Theoretically, it is superior to the cracking process, for irradiation can split hydrocarbon molecules with greater precision, producing increased yields of gasoline at reduced cost. It is for this reason that electron-beam generators are already in operation in the laboratories of large oil refineries. However, their commercial use is limited by the high cost of operation, owing to the great power required.

Another important field in physical chemistry is electrochemistry, which is the science dealing with the relationship between electricity and chemical changes. The reader probably recalls an experiment in electrochemistry performed in his high-school chemistry course, in which a current was sent through a sulphuric acid solution, liberating hydrogen at the cathode and oxygen at the anode. Physical chemists are still seeking a complete explanation of these reactions, which are very complex. Instead of sending a current through a chemical solution, one may reverse the process; chemical reactions themselves may produce a current, as in the case of the ordinary battery cell. These "electrolytic processes," as they are called, have important applications—in the extraction of metals from their ores, in electroplating, and in the refining of steel, as well as in the manufacture of electric batteries. Electrochemical changes are chiefly responsible for corrosion, one of the major production problems in the chemical industry. The physical chemist is peculiarly fitted to help solve these problems because of his understanding of the basic laws and concepts of electrochemistry.

Physical chemists are also concerned with the problems of gases. The kinetic theory of gases, originally developed in the nineteenth century, is a major concept in chemistry today. According to this theory, gas molecules are hard, perfectly elastic spheres, with varying velocities and directions. The physical chemist calculates the number of collisions taking place in an interval of time between gas molecules or between these molecules and a surface. The data he collects are indispensable to the experimental chemist, for he must understand how the gas molecules behave before he can properly interpret chemical reactions involving these gases. The theory has had a great influence in the development of the theory of solution and is in part responsible for the theory of osmosis.

To qualify as a physical chemist, you must have a strong liking for mathematics and physics, as well as for chemistry, and be prepared to take advanced courses in all three subjects. Advanced training is imperative; there are relatively few physical chemists who do not have an M.S. or Ph.D. degree. You should be interested primarily in scientific theory rather than in practical applications—in laws so basic that they apply in all fields of science. To illustrate: your knowledge of the surface tension and other properties of liquids would enable you to determine the behavior not only of chemical solutions in the laboratory but also of sap in trees and of gastric juices in the body.

The Chemist in Atomic Energy

"Chemistry is increasingly important to the peaceful atom. In fact, in the next few years, the chemist may be the most important contributor." [2]

With these words, Dr. Willard F. Libby, chemist and member of the Atomic Energy Commission, underscored the role of the chemist in the important new field of atomic energy. This role is a leading one, because the efficiency of the entire atomic fission operation depends on the choice of proper materials. Chemists are needed in this field primarily to extract, separate, process, treat, refine, and purify elements like uranium, beryllium, zirconium, and halfnium. They seek also to develop new materials that are resistant to very high temperatures and pressures, as well as to corrosion; that do not absorb too many neutrons; that are capable of being fabricated in any desired shape; and that are not too costly. So important is the question of materials in the production of atomic energy that Dr. Edward Teller, so-called "father of the H-bomb," stated recently that chemists as well as metallurgists should replace physicists who are at present directing the construction of nuclear-energy plants, owing to their specialized knowledge of the materials used.

In the design and development of atomic reactors, chemists and chemical engineers are needed to solve the problem of corrosion and deterioration of parts due to long exposure to heat and irradiation. Another challenging problem is that of radioactive hazards caused by chemical reactions. In addition, chemists are seeking to develop new uses for nuclear energy. They are looking forward to the day when chemical reactions will be promoted by the heat of nuclear fission.

The work of the nuclear chemist begins with the uranium ore itself. This is carefully searched for traces of uranium oxide (there is only about a cupful present in each ton). After the uranium is extracted from the uranium oxide, chemists must purify it to the most exacting standard; the impurities remaining must amount to no more than one-millionth of a part. Chemists are needed not only for the preparation of nuclear fuels but also for the recovery of plutonium, which is a by-product of nuclear fission.[3] They are also involved in the problem of the disposal of radio-active wastes. The present method of storing them in tanks is expensive and unsatisfactory. Besides, what is needed are chemical methods of making the wastes not only harmless but also useful for various purposes.

Apart from these considerations, chemists are needed in an expanding field based on the new science of radiochemistry, which deals with the effects of radiation on chemical behavior. One of the most important applications of radiochemistry is the use of radioisotopes (materials made radioactive in atomic reactors) as "tracers"—to chart the complicated course of individual batches of atoms that are radioactively tagged, in chemical or biological reactions. The presence and location of these tagged elements are noted by Geiger counters. This technique, which is so sensitive that it can detect the presence of one-hundred-millionth of an ounce of radioactive material inside a cow weighing 1,000 pounds, has valuable applications in agriculture, medicine, and industry. The tracer may be a single atom sending out signals as it transfers from one molecule to another in a series of chemical reactions—or it may be a molecule of sugar signaling its course of assimilation in the body.

The isotope tracer method "depends very largely on chemistry," [4] owing to the necessity of separating and identifying the different chemical compounds involved. This is often a complicated problem; the tagged molecule may not remain intact or there may be chemical or radiation effects that distort the findings. It is primarily the responsibility of the chemist to see that the results are not spoiled by these factors. Another function of radiochemists is synthesizing compounds containing radioactive elements.

The importance of chemical contributions in this field was high-lighted by the award of the Atoms for Peace Prize in 1950 to Professor Georg von Hevesy of the Research Institute for Organic Chemistry in Stockholm, for developing techniques of using radioactive isotopes in chemistry, biology, and medicine.

At the present time nuclear power is too costly to compete economically with conventional power plants. However, chemists are largely responsible for progress in narrowing this economic gap. They are developing cheaper methods of processing raw materials and reactor fuel, which are the expensive items of nuclear power. In the words of Dr. Libby: "It will likely be the chemist or chemical engineer who will save the final mill per kilowatt hour and make atomic power economical." [5]

The outlook for chemists in the atomic-energy field is a bright one. Authorities predict "a particular need" for chemists and other scientists in this field in the 1960's.[6] Earnings are relatively high; in 1958 they were $11,610 to $12,690 a year for nuclear chemists in basic and applied research. However, this kind of work requires a Ph.D. degree or its equivalent, in addition to special training and experience. Nuclear chemists employed by the AEC develop and supervise chemical-research programs.

Perhaps, as a graduate chemist, you too would be attracted to this field. In 1957 approximately 10 per cent of all chemists and chemical engineers in the United States were in atomic energy. Of all atomic scientists and engineers, chemists and chemical engineers constitute about 30 per cent, an impressive proportion. At the end of 1957, 2,529 chemists and 1,734 chemical engineers were employed by companies having contracts with the AEC, which itself employed 110 chemists and 55 chemical engineers.

The Geochemist

Another fascinating, though small and highly specialized, field in chemistry is geochemistry. This is concerned with the chemical aspects of geology, the science of the earth. As a geochemist you would make chemical studies of the earth's crust or of its interior. You might analyze the material of meteorites or study the development of coal or mineral deposits from decaying animal or vegetable life.

Perhaps you would be employed by the United States

Geological Survey. One of its laboratories is located in Hawaii, and occupies a dramatic perch overlooking the spectacular crater of Kilauea where, far below, lava lakes boil a fiery orange. In this laboratory you would analyze the minute traces of solids and gases that are given off during eruptions. Studies like these enable scientists to probe the secrets of the earth thirty miles or more below the surface and obtain information about its composition and past history.

Geochemical knowledge is important to many scientists —astrophysicists and paleontologists, for example, who are seeking to understand the history of the universe and that of the earth and its inhabitants. Eons ago, the first living things were created. They must have been extremely simple organisms, but even a single cell is made up of remarkably complex organic compounds. How were these compounds first produced and what were the steps in chemical evolution that led to the first spark of living matter? Geochemistry is, in part, concerned with the answers to these questions. Dr. Melvin Calvin, of the University of California, believes that five billion years ago the earth's atmosphere was dominated by hydrogen compounds like methane and ammonia. It was from these substances, he reasons, that the first organic compounds were formed with the aid of lightning or ultraviolet rays—a reaction that can be duplicated today in the laboratory. Dr. Calvin believes also that the evolution of chemicals—up to and including the appearance of the first living cell—took place in a predictable and inevitable manner. It is probable, he adds, that there are a hundred million other planets in the universe with a well-organized life that ranges from microorganisms to sentient beings who are able to speak. His geochemical studies have convinced him that life is, as he puts it, "a state of matter widely distributed throughout the universe."[7]

According to Professor John D. Bernal, of London University, the large molecules created originally from gases in the atmosphere formed fragments of fats and protein. The next stage was the development of cell-like bodies, without membranes, that began to reproduce by cell division; eventually they evolved into more complicated forms and finally became cells like bacteria enclosed in membranes, which constitute the first true organisms. Professor Bernal believed that conditions on this planet were chemically and physically propitious for the emergence of life about 800,000,000 years ago.

Geochemistry is a comparatively new field but one that has become very active in the last ten years. Before World War I, the number of geochemists could have been counted on the fingers of one hand. Even today they probably do not number more than a thousand. Essentially it is a career for the scholarly-minded, for those who love to pursue knowledge for its own sake. To become a geochemist, the chemistry graduate must take advanced courses in geology, in addition to his graduate studies in geochemistry, for geochemistry is a hybrid science that includes physics and geology as well as chemistry. For students with the proper qualifications, it offers the intellectual excitement of one of the most fascinating of all pursuits—a study of the chemical evolution of the earth and of the chemical origin and development of all life.

CHAPTER NINE

The Chemical Engineer

UNTIL NOW, WE HAVE BEEN DISCUSSING THE WORK AND CAREER of the chemist. The reader may have noticed, however, that we often coupled "chemical engineer" with "chemist" in our discussions. The chemical engineer, equally with the chemist, plays a vital role in production, and the work of the two is intimately connected in many areas.

What is a chemical engineer? What kind of work does he do and how does it differ from that of the chemist?

The chemical engineer is concerned with the design, construction, and operation of plants and equipment needed for chemical production. He is an engineer in the full sense of the term and, just like engineers in other fields, handles "unit operations" such as distillation, filtration (the removal of solids from liquids), crystallization (as in the refining of sugar), drying, mixing, and grinding. The chemical engineer controls these operations by means of complex equipment that regulates the temperature, pressure, acidity, and other factors that are important not only in keeping production flowing but also in ensuring uniformity of products. In general, he is responsible for everything that makes for efficient and economic production.

Though he is an engineer, however, he differs from all other types of engineers in that he is also a chemist. The American Chemical Society early admitted chemical engineers to membership on the ground that "a chemical engineer is a chemist as well as an engineer." [1] Graduates from chemical engineering schools are occasionally found in laboratories performing the work of the chemist. On the other hand, a chemist in a small plant may also direct pilot-plant operations, though this is engineering work. The chemical engineer has been defined as a chemist whose operations are on a large scale. As one authority put it: "A chemical engineer ought to know as much engineering as he can but, over and above this—or rather, before this—he must know his chemistry." [2]

One of his main functions is to adapt the chemical reactions that the chemist has developed in the laboratory to large-scale plant operations. The diminutive beakers, flasks, and test tubes are converted into huge tanks, reactors, and coils of pipe. Before designing large-scale equipment, however, the chemical engineer must build a pilot plant. Here the laboratory process is "upscaled" for large production with equipment that simulates, on a much smaller scale, normal plant equipment. He must bear in mind the fact that increasing the volume of chemicals and the size of operations may affect the properties of the product. He must, therefore, be thoroughly familiar with the chemical and physical effects of upscaling. The properties of the manufactured product may be modified by the heating process, by the method used to agitate the chemicals, or by the material used in the enlarged equipment. All these factors must be considered in the design of the pilot plant. After the latter is in operation, improvements are made and shortcomings corrected in accordance with the classic injunction, "Commit your blunders on a small scale and make your profits on a large scale." The pilot plant is a kind of enlarged experimental laboratory in which certain results have to be achieved before large-scale manufacture is initiated.

The chemical engineer in production comes directly up against chemical problems at every turn. When chemicals arrive at a freight station, he must decide how to ship them to the reactors in his plant. The chemicals may be either solid, like sulphur; liquid, like gasoline; or gas, like acetylene, and each type naturally requires a separate handling technique. The chemist in the laboratory heats chemicals electrically; the chemical engineer, operating on a mass scale, must decide whether to use steam, electricity, or hot fluid, depending on which is the safest, the most efficient, and the most economical.

Not only does the chemical engineer design plant equipment; he is also responsible for the material used in its construction. He must decide whether the piping or vessels should be made of steel, of glass-coated metal, of plastic-coated metal or of lead. Selection of the wrong metal may be responsible for corrosion, the bane of the chemical industry which causes great financial losses each year. His choice is guided by chemical rather than by engineering considerations, since it involves the chemical effects of acids, alkalis, and so forth, on various metals.

Chemical engineering is the youngest of all engineering professions, having been born after the turn of the century. Forerunner of today's chemical engineering curriculum was the undergraduate course of study established in 1888 at the Massachusetts Institute of Technology in order to meet "the needs of students who desire a general training in mechanical engineering and, at the same time, wish to devote a portion of their time to a study of the application of chemistry to the arts, especially to those engineering problems which relate to the use and manufacture of chemical products." [3] This was a course in applied chemistry, as much as in chemical engineering, and was administered by the chemical department of M.I.T. Not until the first decade of this century did the modern concept of chemical engineering as a separate branch of engineering begin to take root. The first course of graduate study in chemical engineering was founded in 1912.

Chemical engineers today are employed in all large manufacturing and processing industries that require knowledge of chemistry as well as of mechanical engineering. Their services are needed for scores of industrial processes—the conversion of wood pulp into paper; phosphate rocks into fertilizers; ores into metals; coal, water, and limestone into acetylene. The largest proportion of chemical engineers is in the chemical, petroleum, and pharmaceutical industries.

As a chemical engineer, you would have a choice of careers in the fields of production, research, and development, sales, design, or management. Most engineers are engaged in production, in the supervision and control of chemical operations. They are responsible for keeping production and the quality of the product at high level; for controlling the properties of raw materials entering the plant; for prompt repairs when equipment fails. On the other hand, a significant number of chemical engineers, as well as chemists, are employed as technical salesmen, whose work will be described in a later chapter. Many chemical engineers are top executives, and authorities predict that they will occupy an increasing number of jobs in management. They are employed also by government and research agencies; large cities need chemical engineers for sewerage disposal plants and for the treatment of drinking water. A small percentage of engineers teach in chemical-engineering schools; others become consulting chemical engineers whose services may be used by small concerns unable to afford the expense of maintaining their own engineering staffs, as well as by large concerns. Chemical engineering professors often do consulting work for industrial firms at fees that may amount to more than their annual salaries.

An important, though small, sector of chemical engineering is industrial research, a field that requires keen judgment, imagination, and knowledge based on experience as well as on textbook training. It offers relatively high pay but requires exceptional abilities. An important phase of the work of industrial-research engineers is in developing new, more economical and efficient equipment for chemical processing. Let us say you are doing research for a pump manufacturer. The problem is to design a pump that can transfer mudlike material from the ground to a tank thirty feet high. To select the proper type of pump—and also to determine the size of the electric motor needed to operate it—you would study the "flow" characteristics of the material under different temperatures and pressures and note any corrosive effects on the exposed parts of the pump. For a pump designed to handle radioactive solutions, you might have to develop an original type of machine, based on new pumping principles.

You might instead do industrial research in the metals field. Suppose that your assignment in this field is the development of an alloy that will be resistant to the corrosive effects of hydrogen-chloride solutions. You would prepare different metal alloys, expose them to the solutions, and inspect them under the microscope to note any effects. A chemical engineer developed a standard test now used in the metals industry to determine whether sufficient heat treatment has been given to stainless steel to make it resistant to corrosion. Corrosion, as we have seen, is one of the most serious problems in production. If the metal used in equipment is not sufficiently resistant to chemicals and heat, serious financial losses may result because the equipment must be replaced. Chemical engineers must therefore make elaborate studies of the various kinds of metals, using instruments like the electron microscope before selecting the proper alloy for each piece of equipment needed.

One of the most active fields in chemical engineering is the management of production. In this capacity you would be responsible for the proper maintenance, staffing, and servicing of your department. You would have to cope with a great variety of problems, and to solve most of them without delay. In a single day you might have to deal with such varied problems as the report that a shipment of chemicals has failed to meet specifications; another report of corrosion in a high-vacuum still, which you would have to inspect and repair temporarily until a new still arrived; a doctor's complaint of toxic vapors in one of the departments, caused by inadequate ventilation (you might have to order respirators and protective skin cream for the operators until a new ventilation system was installed); the appointment of a new foreman; and an unexpected rush order for chemicals from a large pharmaceutical company.

This kind of work is obviously not for the scholar who enjoys leisure and meditation. It would attract those who prefer the excitement of working under pressure at a variety of tasks, in planning, administration, procurement, sales, production, research, and development. To cope with these problems, the chemical engineer in charge of production must have a variety of skills. He must be able to handle sudden emergencies, to write reports that are logical and concise, to handle the repair of machinery, to persuade people and win their confidence. The job calls for fast thinking and quick decisions, as well as for dependability and executive efficiency.

Chemical engineers as well as chemists play important

roles in the atomic-energy field. A major chemical engineering achievement in this area was the separation of tiny amounts of uranium 235 from ordinary uranium. At first, physical methods were tried, but they proved unsuccessful and the yield was too small. A breakthrough came when chemical engineers devised the "gaseous diffusion method," which requires the use of special materials in the construction of equipment. Even more remarkable was the accomplishment of chemical engineers in separating plutonium from the products of a reaction pile on a large scale. The properties of plutonium were unknown at that time, and chemists had to determine them on the basis of millionth-of-a-gram samples, as there was no opportunity to check with larger samples, owing to war emergencies. Trusting that these findings were correct, chemical engineers built a full-scale plant at Hanford, Washington, without first building a pilot plant, for which there was no time. Their efforts met with success, constituting a brilliant feat of chemical engineering—one that required the closest cooperation between chemists and chemical engineers.[4]

Chemical engineers have been in increasing demand in the pharmaceutical industry, especially in recent years. The number of chemical engineers employed by Charles Pfizer and Company, one of the largest pharmaceutical organizations in the country, rose from 44 in 1947 to 145 in 1955. These engineers were confronted with problems that were novel and even unprecedented, owing to the uniqueness of the products; 80 per cent of the company's sales at this writing are of products that were not even on the market before 1942, and their manufacture has required new processes and techniques.

A basic process used in the Pfizer plant is fermentation, which is used to extract penicillin and other antibiotics from their molds. Fermentation is also combined with other processes in the synthesis of antibiotics and hormones—an important advance, as synthesis can be accomplished by conventional methods only with great difficulty. The separation of ingredients by means of fermentation is an extremely difficult process, requiring great ingenuity and resourcefulness because of the unusually low concentration of the ingredients. For example, magnesium is present in sea water in the proportions of 1,270 parts per million, but the concentration of vitamin B_{12} in a fermentation broth is in the proportion of 1 part per million!

A significant feature of the chemical-engineering profession is the relatively large number of engineers who have advanced degrees. In spite of the fact that it is the youngest of all branches of engineering, relatively more chemical engineers have M.S. or Ph.D. degrees than engineers in any other branch. In 1957 the number of students taking graduate courses was three times the number of all students enrolled in engineering schools in 1910, showing the huge strides taken by the profession since that time.[5] The fact that approximately 35 per cent of the members of chemical engineering societies hold advanced degrees underscores the importance of graduate training in this field. Graduate training leads to higher salaries and offers greater opportunities for advancement. This is shown by the following figures, representing the median salaries per month for chemical engineers with different degrees in 1956:

Chemical engineers with a B.S. degree $425.00
Chemical engineers with an M.S. degree 485.00
Chemical engineers with a Ph.D. degree 604.00

Over 80 per cent of all chemical engineers are employed in the manufacturing field. About 32 per cent of these engineers occupy administrative jobs—a higher proportion than in any other field of engineering. This is significant because earnings are generally higher on the administrative level.

It may happen that you are attracted to the chemical field but cannot make up your mind whether to become a chemist or a chemical engineer. The answer to the problem lies in an analysis of your chief inclinations and interests. You must ask yourself: "Do I get my main 'kick' in school from pursuing knowledge for its own sake, from studying the laws of nature and conducting laboratory experiments?" If the answer is "Yes," then you would probably be happier as a chemist. If, on the other hand, you have an essentially practical bent and are as much interested in mechanics and in machine processes as you are in chemistry, you probably should become a chemical engineer instead. Aptitude tests are often of value in helping a student decide on the exact choice of a career but, as stated in a previous chapter, they are not infallible. In any event, you should make up your mind whether you wish to become a chemist or a chemical engineer, before graduating from high school, for the engineering college course is different and separate from the course in chemistry and the two courses are not interchangeable. Lists of accredited schools both of chemistry and of chemical engineering are given in the Appendix.

As in other fields of engineering, the demand for chemical engineers may fluctuate in different periods. It rose considerably in the early fifties; this is reflected in the figures for starting salaries, which increased 20 per cent from 1952 to 1956. From a long-range viewpoint, the need for chemical engineers will rise steadily with the anticipated growth and expansion of the chemical and allied industries, which owe much to the chemical engineer for their phenomenal growth since the last world war. As stated in a report by industrial and scientific authorities in 1952: "The leading position in the chemical industrial field that the United States has acquired in recent years, is to a great extent due to the rapid development of the profession of chemical engineering." [6]

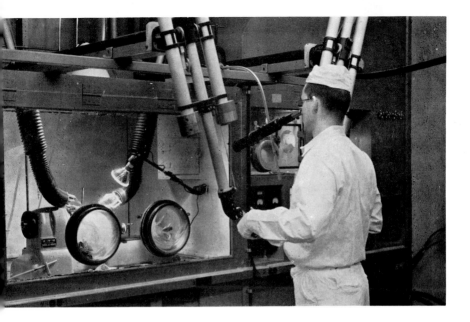

Above. Chemist operating a manipulator in the fabrication of radioactive material. The "cave" and the two windows of double thicknesses of glass with water between them protect him from the dangerous radiations. Chemists play an important role in the atomic energy field. *(Courtesy Monsanto Chemical Company and U. S. Atomic Energy Commission)* *Below.* Chemical engineer at work in a pilot plant which simulates large-scale production. *(Courtesy Union Carbide Corporation)*

Above. Chemical salesmen serve as important links between the research laboratory and the consumer. Here a chemical salesman demonstrates how a certain compound makes a paper bag water-repellant, while the manager of a department in a bag company watches intently. *(Courtesy E. I. du Pont de Nemours and Company, Inc.) Below.* Women make excellent chemists. Here a woman chemist examines a sample of oil to note the effects of chemical additives on the rate at which it "burns." *(Courtesy Union Carbide Corporation)*

CHAPTER TEN

The Chemist as Technical Salesman

So far, we have been discussing the chemist as a scientist in a laboratory, who works either in the production, research, or development department. It is important to remember, however, that chemistry is not only Science but also Big Business; it needs salesmen, sales managers, executives, and administrators to sell the chemicals that flow in an endless stream from the plants, and to develop and expand new markets for them. There was a time when chemists were divorced from management and their place was exclusively in the laboratory. Then came the phenomenal growth and expansion of the chemical industry, and demand arose not only for laboratory chemists but also for a chemically trained sales and administrative personnel, to bridge the gap between the research laboratory and the market for its products.

Let us suppose that a chemical company decides to manufacture a new drug that has important uses both in medicine and in agriculture. The research and development chemist having done his job, it is now up to other chemists, as technical salesmen and market experts, to carry it through to success. A new sales and marketing program has to be developed. Technical groups must be organized to advise

117

medical, industrial, and agricultural officials about the uses and advantages of the new product. A special corps of professional representatives who are experts in nutrition and medicine may have to be formed to explain its value to doctors and pharmacists. Still another group must be organized to bring the drug to the attention of farmers and feed manufacturers. Finally, distribution centers must be built in key states, so as to ensure speedy delivery of drugs at the market. All this requires the services of chemists who are also salesmen and executives.

To develop this new type of chemist-executive-salesman, the big companies assign chemists to production departments so that they can become familiar with the concrete problems of manufacturing. They are then transferred to the sales department and become technical salesmen for a year or so. This gives them the opportunity to study the needs of customers, to be able to answer their questions and help iron out their problems. With this background of manufacturing, administrative, and sales experience, they become qualified for important jobs outside the laboratory; they may become salesmen, sales managers, plant managers, or heads of divisions in the company.

As a chemistry graduate, you might be attracted to the job of technical salesman rather than that of laboratory chemist. The word "salesman" seems an inappropriate term for a scientist, but the technical salesman is a different species from his high-pressure namesake in other fields. He is not only a salesman but a market-research man, a technical consultant, a credit investigator, and a public-relations man, all rolled into one. Fifty years ago there were comparatively few chemicals on the market, and the chemical salesman did not require more than a high-school education for his job. Today the volume and variety of chemicals and chemical products on the market are almost endless. To be able to give information about them and sell them successfully, the salesman must be a trained chemist with an academic degree. Among his customers may be research chemists, as well as production men and business executives in top managerial posts; he must be able to talk their language and understand their manufacturing and marketing, as well as their scientific, problems. Chemicals are sold to specialized industries, and the salesman must also have some knowledge of the technical needs of these industries. To his customers he is a source of valuable information, as well as a salesman, and they are in the habit of consulting him as a technical adviser.

Consider a problem as simple as that of charcoal. Joe Jones, the chief chemist of a company that manufactures a chemical for household use, is in need of charcoal to absorb the color from the chemical, so that it will be white in appearance. He knows that there are dozens of kinds and grades on the market. What kind should he select for his purpose? He consults Harry Smith, chemist and technical salesman of a large chemical company, for Smith has a thorough knowledge of the different grades, and understands their advantages and limitations. He advises Jones regarding the proper selection. In the course of his conversation, he might suggest methods of saving money that had not occurred to Jones, in spite of his experience in the matter.

As a technical salesman, you would have the responsibility of maintaining good will and mollifying the customer if something went wrong, such as a delay in shipment or the failure of materials to meet exact specifications. You would be on friendly terms with your customers, owing to your technical ability to help them in various ways. Some chemistry graduates are temperamentally more fitted for this kind of work than for laboratory work, which they may

find too confining. For them the career of technical salesman has definite advantages, combining as it does the
satisfaction of applying scientific and technical knowledge
with the pleasure of social contacts. In addition, the work
may be very remunerative and may advance them to a
post on the top management level.

The career of Hugh D. Hughes points up these satisfac-
tions and rewards. Mr. Hughes graduated *magna cum laude*
from Wesleyan University in 1920, with a degree in chemistry, receiving an M.S. the following year. He began as a
chemist in process development but went on the road as a
technical salesman for Carbide and Carbon Chemicals Corporation in 1929. Later he was advanced to the positions
of district manager and division manager, and in 1945 he
became a sales manager. Eight years later he was appointed
general sales manager of industrial chemicals. Mr. Hughes
can look back on a rich and fruitful career, in which science,
business, and social relationships were agreeably mixed.

Technical salesmen are in a strategic position to advance
themselves in the company, as Mr. Hughes did, and a large
proportion of highly paid executives with chemical companies formerly worked as salesmen. Many technical salesmen receive a comparatively high salary, for in recent years
the sales of chemicals have advanced spectacularly, rising
by more than 129 per cent from 1945 to 1951—the increase
each year averaging over three times the annual increase in
other manufacturing fields. It is easy to understand the need
for salesmen, when we consider that, during this period,
the six largest chemical companies more than doubled their
sales. (Du Pont sales alone increased by almost a billion
dollars.)

Instead of becoming a technical salesman, you might
work in the area known as commercial chemical development. This is concerned with the production, promotion,

and sale of new chemical products. You would engage in promotional sales work and market research and development. Like the salesman, you would assist customers, advise them, and handle complaints of a technical nature. Basically, however, your work would consist of evaluating the commercial possibilities of new products, finding markets for them, and developing demand among the customers. For example, you would persuade them to buy chemical samples for the purpose of testing them in their pilot plants. This is often more difficult to accomplish than selling them carload quantities after a product has proved itself, and is in wide demand. As a commercial chemical development man, you would be preparing the ground for the salesmen and laying the basis for future large-scale orders.

If this kind of work appealed to you more than a career in straight selling, you would be in the technical and development department, which is midway between the research and the sales departments. Your job would involve correlating experimental work with research and sales; you would work at different times in each of these areas. Officials at Dow Chemical Company estimate that from 30 per cent to 60 per cent of such a chemist's time is spent in its laboratory; 20 per cent to 30 per cent, in consultation with the research, production, and sales departments; and the remaining 20 per cent to 30 per cent, with the customers who ask him to arrange demonstrations and testing of the products in their own plants. Becoming familiar with the work in all these departments and understanding their interrelationships would give you exceptional training and experience, and qualify you later for the highest administrative positions. Obviously, not every chemistry graduate has the necessary traits for work in this field. A chemist may be a whiz when it comes to synthesizing a new compound but a dud when it comes to estimating its commercial possibilities. The job of commercial chemical development requires a combination of sales ability with business, academic, and technical training.

The organization that represents chemists in this field is the Commercial Chemical Development Association. Its president from 1949 to 1950 was Charles D. Goodale, who has shown by his own record of achievement how far a qualified chemist can advance in this field. Goodale received two degrees from Purdue University, after which he worked in the process chemical laboratory of a large company. Later he switched to the research department and then to the sales-development division. In this way he received a well-rounded training that qualified him for his next job, that of manager of the technical service division. Mr. Goodale's own experience is evidence in support of his view that a chemistry graduate will advance further if he works in as many fields as possible, before deciding on a particular specialty.

It is significant that both Mr. Goodale and Mr. Hughes, the former in commercial development and the latter in technical sales, not only are chemistry graduates but also have advanced degrees. This points up the fact that advanced academic training is as important in chemical business areas as in the laboratory. In the old days the college-trained salesman was regarded as an oddity. Today professional education and training are indispensable for such a job. The chemical salesman will be judged on the basis of his sales record; but, without adequate education and training, he will not be able to sell effectively and will have far less chance of advancement to higher positions with the company. Selling chemicals, in short, is a profession that requires academic training. In recent years it has attracted a growing number of graduate chemists. As one authority stated in a symposium, "Frequently, as many graduate chemists will be found in a company's sales department as in its research and development laboratories." [1]

By selling chemicals that improve food, textiles, metals, and other basic materials, the salesman has the satisfaction of knowing that he is not only making a good living but also contributing to economic and social progress. Besides, the greater the sales volume, the more appropriations are available for research and development. The salesman thus indirectly supports the research chemist, just as the discoveries made by the research chemist increase the need for salesmen. To quote Lester E. Johnson, president of the Commercial Chemical Development Association: "Research expense cannot be recovered unless a reasonable proportion of laboratory ideas are converted into saleable materials and a goodly number of research reports are eventually transformed into production plants." [2]

In addition to the business careers mentioned, there are many other fields of opportunity outside the laboratory that beckon to the graduate chemist. Thus, chemists are needed for chemical public relations or publicity work; for sales promotion, involving the preparation of booklets, brochures, and promotional letters; for technical advertising; as chemical stock specialists in Wall Street offices. Chemists may also specialize as experts in litigation proceedings that involve infringements on patents and may receive anywhere from $100 to $1,000 a day for their testimony. On the other hand, chemists with a flair for writing are in demand to fill positions on the editorial staffs of chemical journals, house organs, and similar publications. The graduate chemist thus faces a wide choice of career opportunities, depending on whether he likes laboratory work, research, production, development, writing, selling, business, technical consultation, public relations, or legal technicalities, in addition to chemistry.

CHAPTER ELEVEN

Calling All Women Chemists!

AT A RECENT CONFERENCE OF CHEMISTS AND ENGINEERS, THE chairman opened the meeting as follows: "*Lady* and gentlemen"! The single lady present, to whom the chairman referred, was Miss Betty Lou Raskin, chemist of the radiation laboratory of Johns Hopkins University. The rest of the audience of two thousand people consisted of males.[1]

This situation is not unusual. Social habit and custom have reinforced the widespread assumption that science as well as engineering is for males only. One result of this attitude is that only about 5 per cent of all members of the American Chemical Society are women—this in spite of the fact that many women have proved their competence as chemists and some have received the highest recognition and awards, including the Nobel Prize, for their contributions.

The truth of the matter is that women are temperamentally suited for careers in chemistry. Some of the traits needed for such a career are peculiarly characteristic of womankind in general: patience, conscientiousness, meticulousness, neatness, a capacity for keen observation, for at-

124

tention to fine details, and for teamwork. Women are qualified not only for laboratory work but also for other activities in the chemical field, such as teaching, library work, technical writing, and administrative work. As to research, women chemists have made important contributions in this field. Said Dr. Augustus B. Kinzel, vice president for research of the Union Carbide Corporation: "Of course, women can do research! Whether it is basic, experimental or analytical research, their native logic is every bit as good as men's; their intuition, frequently better." [2]

It is a curious fact that, in spite of these considerations, relatively few women choose chemistry, or indeed any other science, as a career. Only 4 per cent of all women college graduates in 1955–1956 had majored in science, and only 397 women out of a group of 70,043 college graduates in 1956 became chemists. A significant reason for this state of affairs was stated in a 1954 report of a conference of employers and educators at Bryn Mawr College, as follows:

"One of the greatest obstacles in the way of educating women in scientific fields has been the persistence of certain outmoded conceptions in the minds of students, their parents and even some employers and educators. . . . Among these are the beliefs that it is not womanly to study science; that there is no cultural value in the study of the physical world in which we live, and that there are no really good opportunities for women in scientific fields." [3]

Discussing the paucity of female chemists, Eleanor F. Horsey and Donna Price stated in 1946 that the number of women chemists could be increased tenfold if all girls with the potential ability chose chemistry as a career. "When women are encouraged to enter scientific professions," they said, "and when they no longer encounter the obstacles we have mentioned, the country may expect 40,000 apprentice scientists annually from their ranks." Other authorities have said that for every girl who becomes a chemist, there are many others who would like to do so but are held back by the notion that the door to every career in science bears the unwritten label "For men only."

It was only because there was a shortage of male chemists that the demand for women chemists rose sharply during World War II. In a report to the American Chemical Society at the time, Dr. Helen I. Miner said, prophetically: "Conclusion of the war will not contract this extended horizon for women chemists. In the reconstruction period which must follow, there will be acute need for trained Americans of both sexes to assist in the multitude of problems—nutritional, agricultural and industrial—which must be solved in winning the peace." History has confirmed the correctness of this analysis. The number of women in chemistry today, while relatively small, is larger than in any other scientific field and is several times the number before the war.

That women have the intellectual capacity to make important contributions in chemistry has been amply demonstrated by numerous women chemists, ever since Marie Sklodowska Curie, in cooperation with her husband, Pierre, discovered radium and was awarded the Nobel Prize in chemistry in 1911. One woman chemist of particular distinction is Dr. Maria Telkes, who came to this country with a Ph.D. degree in physical chemistry from the University of Budapest and became one of the leading authorities in the field of solar energy. She is particularly known for her success in converting the sun's radiation directly into electricity. As a civilian adviser in the Office of Science and Research Development during the war, she devised a sun-heated distilling system that converted sea water into drinking water.

Then there is Miss Haylande D. Young, one of the many

women chemists cited in *American Men of Science*. (Query: Why not *American Men and Women of Science*? Dr. Young has won distinction as a chemist in an impressive variety of fields—organic chemistry, biochemistry, petroleum, toxicity of chemicals, and atomic energy. In addition to working in private industry, she has taught at college and has done research in university laboratories. Included among her many activities have been pilot-plant development work, supervising and policy-making. Since 1945 she has been associated with the Argonne National Laboratory in atomic-energy projects.

Another distinguished woman chemist is Sister M. Joan Preising, O.S.F., professor of chemistry and head of the chemistry department at the College of St. Francis, of Joliet, Illinois. In 1958 she received the first "Chemists of the Year" award from the Joliet Section of the American Chemical Society. Sister Joan was cited for her teaching, research activities, and writings. Then there is Miss Donna Cosulich, senior research chemist at Lederle's Laboratories at Pearl River, New York. In 1958 she was awarded a grant by the American Cyanamid Corporation for the purpose of studying at the University of Geneva and doing research in methods of analyzing alkaloids and antibiotics. An honorary fraternity voted Miss Cosulich "the outstanding young woman chemist in the United States" in 1945. There are scores of others—Dr. Taisia Stadnichenko of the United States Geological Survey, for example, who discovered the metal germanium in coal ashes and in the wood of certain prehistoric trees. Dr. Dorothy Wrinch, a biochemist, made important investigations of insulin and proteins. Among many women chemists listed in *American Men of Science* is Dr. H. Marjorie Crawford, who began her schooling at an ungraded country school in a small village in Ohio and became a distinguished research chemist and chairman of the Department of Chemistry at Vassar College.

Some employers, though fortunately to a limited extent, hesitate to employ women chemists for fear that they will quit their jobs as soon as they get married and begin raising a family. While such an attitude is understandable, the findings of a survey conducted under the auspices of the Social Science Research Council showed that the turnover of manpower was practically the same as that of woman-power in certain areas. In the words of the National Man-power Council: "The available evidence indicates that on the average, women are no more likely than men to quit their jobs." The council added that "during the last decade, the differences in turnover rates between men and women workers in manufacturing have declined." [4]

Prejudice by employers against women chemists has diminished greatly since the First World War. Women today "are apparently gaining increasing acceptance in research in chemistry and biology." [5] This is part of a general trend. To quote Miss Alice K. Leopold, Director of the Women's Bureau of the United States Department of Labor: "The widening of job horizons for women is one of the most striking developments of recent years. More and more, emphasis is placed on qualifications, training and experience, regardless of whether an employee is a man or a woman. In order to qualify for the new employment opportunities opening in our highly developed society, women must secure education and training appropriate to their abilities and interests." [6]

Marriage and even the raising of a family are no longer bars to successful careers. A survey of women chemistry graduates from Hunter College from 1940 to 1955 revealed the fact that 74 per cent were married and each had an average of two children; yet more than half of them were employed in 1958 in various fields of chemistry, with a median income of from $4,500 to $5,500 a year.

The largest percentage of women chemists are in research and development work. This is shown by the following table, which gives the percentage distribution of female members of the American Chemical Society in various specialized fields in 1955:

Special Field	Percentage of Women Chemists
Research and Development	39.4%
Analysis and Testing	19.3%
Teaching	16.9%
Library work	9.8%
Administrative work	4.6%
Other types of work	10.0%

The number of women chemists who received bachelor's degrees in chemistry rose to a peak in 1950 and then declined in the succeeding years, though the number of male graduates continued to rise. This is shown by the following figures: [8]

Number of Graduate Chemists
with B.S. Degree

	1942	1944	1950	1956
Men	3,281	2,474	3,343	5,618
Women	835	1,237	7,451	1,182
TOTAL	4,116	3,711	10,794	6,800

Women chemists receive less pay than their male colleagues—and the disparity increases with length of experience. Thus, after twenty-four years, the median salary for male chemists is $9,500 as against $6,000 for women chemists. This is a deplorable fact. Not only is the disparity unjust; it is hardly calculated to help us overcome the shortage of chemists by attracting women into the field! It is also true, however, that women chemists earn more than any other group of female scientists.

Income disparity between the sexes is relatively small for beginning salaries, as indicated by the following figures for comparative median starting salaries for chemists of both sexes and for different years:

	1943	1956	1957
Men chemists	$2,076	$4,884	$5,280
Women chemists	1,884	4,500	4,800

Not only are many girls potentially good scientists but some are unusually talented. This was demonstrated recently when 158 high-school students, ranging in age from twelve to eighteen, took part in a college-science program at Columbia University Engineering School. Twenty-five of these students were girls. Every Saturday they attended free lectures given by Columbia professors and conducted supervised laboratory experiments. The lectures dealt with advanced subjects, including nuclear physics and protein chemistry. The results were characterized by an assistant dean as "staggering." All but a handful scored higher marks than the average college freshman.[9] The experiment would seem to corroborate the claim of authorities that what keeps many girls from becoming chemists is not lack of ability or other qualifications but lack of proper guidance, especially at the high-school level.

Women as Chemical Engineers

Women make not only good chemists but also good chemical engineers. This may surprise some people who regard engineering as a male occupation. The fact is, however, that about 6 per cent of all engineers in the country are women. There are women electrical, mechanical, chemical, civil, mining, petroleum, and industrial engineers.

The percentage would be higher were it not for lack of proper vocational guidance. According to Professor Cecile Froelich, Chairman of the Department of Electrical Engineering of the City College of New York, the comparatively small number of women in engineering is due not to lack of acceptance by employers but to the fact that "the majority of high school girls never learn about the opportunities in engineering and so they neglect suitable preparations." Professor Froelich feels that several branches of engineering, including chemical engineering, are ideally suited for women, and notes that in normal times women with engineering degrees do not find it difficult to obtain employment; indeed, industrial firms may be "eager to have them, sometimes signing them to contracts even before they have their degrees." She reports that girls who are not told the advantages of engineering as a suitable profession, while at high school, and who later decide to become engineers, discover too often that they lack some of the courses necessary for admission into engineering colleges.

Another distinguished authority who holds this view is Dr. Arthur S. Flemming, former director of the Office of Defense Mobilization. "There is no question at all," he said, "but that more women should be enrolled in our engineering schools. This is one of the ways of dealing adequately with the present and potential shortages in this area." He added that schools and colleges should improve their vocational guidance services, and encourage girls with an aptitude for engineering to enter the profession. In the words of still another authority: "Thousands of women who receive degrees in mathematics and science might have become good engineers if they had been advised of their capabilities and informed that the profession is open to them." [10]

The vast extent of unused engineering talent among females is reflected in the small percentage of women college students who take engineering courses of *any* kind. Of the 19,707 engineering degrees that were conferred in 1954, only 57 were awarded to women. This in spite of the fact that more than 124,000 women graduate from college each year!

As an indication of what women can accomplish as chemical engineers, consider the career of Dr. Margaret H. Hutchinson. After graduating from Rice Institute with a B.S. in chemistry, she took graduate courses for a degree in chemical engineering, and was the first woman ever to receive a Doctor of Science degree in this field from M.I.T. After graduating, she directed research and development projects and later became a senior process engineer in chemical plants. Dr. Hutchinson is at present a chemical-engineering consultant. She is the author of numerous papers published in technical journals and was the first woman to be accepted as an active member by the American Institute of Chemical Engineers. In 1955 she won an Achievement Award from the Society of Women Engineers for her contributions.

More women chemists and more women chemical engineers! This is the answer to the problem of manpower shortages in these scientific fields, in the opinion of many authorities.

In Conclusion

We have shown that chemistry and chemical engineering have produced revolutionary changes both in our way of life and in our knowledge of matter and of the universe.

Their offspring, the chemical industry, has expanded into one of our major and fundamental industries, and one which has affected the development of all other sectors of our economy. Paralleling this expansion has been the growth of the chemical profession itself and the specialization of its fields of activity.

In the words of Dr. James Bryant Conant, eminent chemist and president of Harvard University: "The growth of the chemical profession within the lifetime of many of us has been one of the amazing social phenomena of our times. It takes no crystal ball to show that this chemical revolution will affect the balance of the century. Whether the curve will continue to mount at the same rate of annual change is an open question; but one of the few certainties of the future seems to be that there will be vastly more citizens of this nation who are trained as chemists and chemical engineers in 2001 than there are now in 1951. . . . The breadth of his scientific training and the strategic position of his science will make him [the chemist] one of the key figures in an urbanized, mechanized society, dependent for its very life on the careful control of a multitude of chemical reactions." [11]

Appendix

LISTED BELOW ARE INSTITUTIONS GRANTING DEGREES IN CHEMISTRY
that are approved by the American Chemical Society. Included
also are those granting degrees in chemical engineering that are
accredited by the American Institute of Chemical Engineers.

Students should note that many institutions not on the approved list give excellent courses in chemistry but do not prepare students for professional work in chemistry. Their graduates may, however, go on to complete their professional training in graduate schools and they may eventually become fully
trained and qualified chemists. Note also that some institutions
are fully qualified to appear on the list but are not included
because the request for such inclusion has not been made
through the proper channels.

In view of the above, the high-school student interested in a
career in chemistry or in chemical engineering is strongly advised to make inquiries of the college of his choice and obtain
full particulars about its status. He should check also with the
American Chemical Society, 1155 Sixteenth Street, N.W., Washington 6, D.C.

Graduates with a bachelor's degree in chemistry from institutions on the approved list are eligible for membership in the

American Chemical Society (provided they are certified by their department chairman as having fulfilled ACS requirements for professional training) after two years of experience in chemistry or in chemical engineering or in postgraduate work. The same applies to graduates with a degree in chemical engineering from institutions on the list. Graduates from institutions *not* on the list are eligible for membership in the ACS only after five years of experience in chemistry or chemical engineering.

Note: Names that are in parentheses are of institutions that are accredited *only* for chemical engineering. Institutions giving courses in chemical engineering that are accredited by the Institute of Chemical Engineers and by the Engineers Council for Professional Development are indicated by (X).

AGNES SCOTT College
Akron, University of
Alabama Polytechnic Institute   (X)
Alabama, University of (X)
Albion College
Allegheny College
Amherst College
Antioch College
Arizona State University
Arizona, University of
Arkansas, University of (X)
Augustana College

BALDWIN-WALLACE College
Barnard College
Bates College
Baylor University
Beloit College
Boston College
Boston University
Bowdoin College
Bowling Green State University
Bradley University
Brandeis University
Brigham Young University
Brooklyn College
Brooklyn, Polytechnic Institute of (X)

Brown University
Bryn Mawr College
Bucknell University (X)
Buffalo, University of

CALIFORNIA Institute of Technology (X)
California, University of (Berkeley) (X)
California, University of (Davis)
California, University of (Los Angeles)
California, University of (Santa Barbara College)
Calvin College
Carleton College
Carnegie Institute of Technology (X)
Case Institute of Technology (X)
Catholic University of America
Central State College
Chatham College
Chicago, University of
Cincinnati, University of (X)
Citadel, The
City College of the City of New York (X)
Clark University

Clarkson College of Technology
(X)
Clemson Agricultural College
Coe College
Colby College
Colgate University
Colorado College
(Colorado School of Mines) (X)
Colorado State University
Colorado, University of (X)
Columbia University (X)
Connecticut, University of (X)
(Cooper Union for the Advance-
ment of Science and Art) (X)
Cornell University (X)

DARTMOUTH College
Davidson College
Delaware, University of (X)
Denison University
Denver, University of
De Paul University
DePauw University
Detroit, University of (X)
Dickinson College
Douglass College
Drew University
(Drexel Institute of Technology)
(X)
Duke University
Duquesne University

EMORY University

(FENN College) (X)
Florida State University
Florida, University of (X)
Fordham, University
Franklin and Marshall College

GENEVA College
Georgia Institute of Technology
(X)
Georgia, University of
Gettysburg College

Gonzaga University
Grinnell College

HAMILTON College
Hamline University
Harvard University
Haverford College
Hawaii, University of
Holy Cross, College of the
Hope College
Houston, University of (X)
Howard University
Hunter College

IDAHO, University of (X)
Illinois Institute of Technology (X)
Illinois, University of (X)
Indiana University
Iowa State College (X)
Iowa, State University of (X)

JOHNS HOPKINS University
Juniata College

KANSAS CITY, University of
Kansas State College (X)
Kansas, University of (X)
Kent State University
Kentucky, University of
Kenyon College
Knox College

LAFAYETTE College (X)
Lawrence College
Lehigh University (X)
Louisiana Polytechnic Institute
(X)
Louisiana State University (X)
Louisville, University of (X)
Loyola University (Chicago)
Loyola University of Los Angeles
Loyola University of the South

MACALESTER College
Maine, University of (X)

Marquette University
Maryland, University of (X)
Massachusetts Institute of Technology (X)
Massachusetts, University of
Miami University
Miami, University of
Michigan College of Mining and Technology (X)
Michigan State University of Agriculture and Applied Science (X)
Michigan, University of (X)
Middlebury College
Mills College
Minnesota, University of (X)
Minnesota, University of (Duluth branch)
Mississippi State University
Mississippi, University of (X)
Missouri School of Mines and Metallurgy (X)
Missouri, University of (X)
Monmouth College
Montana State College (X)
Montana State University
Morgan State College
Mount Holyoke College
Mount Union College
Muhlenberg College

NEBRASKA, University of (X)
Nevada, University of
New Hampshire, University of
New Mexico College of Agriculture and Mechanic Arts
New Mexico Highlands University
New Mexico Institute of Mining and Technology
New Mexico, University of
New York University, University college (X)
New York University, Washington Square College

Newark College of Arts and Sciences
(Newark College of Engineering) (X)
Newcomb College
North Carolina State College (X)
North Carolina, University of
North Dakota Agricultural College
North Dakota, University of (X)
North Texas State College
Northeastern University (X)
Northwestern University (X)
Norwich University
Notre Dame, University of (X)

OBERLIN College
Occidental College
Ohio State University (X)
Ohio University
Ohio Wesleyan University
Oklahoma State University (X)
Oklahoma, University of (X)
Oregon State College (X)
Oregon, University of

PACIFIC, College of the
Pennsylvania State University (X)
    Chemistry Department
    Agricultural and Biological Chemistry Department
Pennsylvania, University of (X)
Philadelphia College of Pharmacy and Science
Pittsburgh, University of (X)
Pomona College
Portland, University of
(Pratt Institute) (X)
Princeton University (X)
Providence College
Puget Sound, College of
Purdue University (X)

QUEENS College

RADCLIFFE College
Randolph-Macon Women's College

Redlands, University of
Reed College
Rensselaer Polytechnic Institute (X)
Rhode Island, University of (X)
Rice Institute, The (X)
Richmond, University of (X)
Rochester, University of (X)
(Rose Polytechnic Institute) (X)
Rutgers University

ST. JOHN'S College, St. John's University
St. Joseph's College
Saint Louis College
Saint Olaf College
Saint Peter's College
Saint Thomas, College of
San Diego State College
San Francisco, University of
San Jose State College
Seattle University
Seton Hall University
Smith College
South Carolina, University of (X)
South Dakota School of Mines and Technology
South Dakota State College of Agriculture and Mechanic Arts
South Dakota, State University of
Southern California, University of
Southern Illinois University
Southern Methodist University
Southwestern Louisiana Institute (X)
Stanford University
Swarthmore College
Syracuse University (X)

TEMPLE University
Tennessee Polytechnic Institute
Tennessee, University of (X)
Texas, Agricultural and Mechanical College of (X)
Texas Christian University
Texas Technological College

Texas, University of (X)
Texas Woman's University
Toledo, University of
Trinity College
Tufts University (X)
Tulane University (X)
Tulsa, University of

UNION College
Ursinus College
Utah State University
Utah, University of (X)

VALPARAISO University
Vanderbilt University
Vassar College
Vermont, University of
Villanova University (X)
Virginia Military Institute
Virginia Polytechnic Institute (X)
Virginia, University of (X)

WABASH College
Washington and Lee University
Washington, State College of (X)
Washington University (X)
Washington, University of (X)
Wayne State University (X)
Wellesley College
Wesleyan University
West Virginia University (X)
Western Kentucky State College (X)
Western Kentucky State College
Western Reserve University
Wheaton College (Illinois)
Wheaton College (Massachusetts)
Wichita, University of
William and Mary, College of
Williams College
Wilson College
Wisconsin, University of (X)
Wooster, College of
Worcester Polytechnic Institute (X)
Wyoming, University of
YALE University (X)

Notes and References

CHAPTER ONE

[1] Bernard Jaffe, *Crucibles: The Story of Chemistry* (New York: Simon and Schuster, Inc., 1948), p. 16.

[2] W. T. Sedgwick and H. W. Tyler, *A Short History of Science* (New York: The Macmillan Company, 1939), p. 28.

[3] *Ibid.*, p. 62.

[4] *Ibid.*, p. 165.

[5] *Ibid.*, pp. 253–254.

[6] *Ibid.*, p. 410.

CHAPTER TWO

[1] *Chemical and Engineering News*, September 17, 1951, p. 3847.

[2] Anthony Standen, "The First Seventy-five Years," *Chemical and Engineering News*, August 13, 1951, p. 3242.

[3] *Chemical and Engineering News*, September 17, 1951, p. 3848.

[4] *Scientific Personnel Resources*, National Science Foundation, 1955, p. 27.

[5] *Science and Engineering in American Industry* (1953–1954 Survey), National Science Foundation, p. 77.

[6] Leland I. Doan, editor, *Chemistry's Role in Better Living: A Symposium* (Troy, N.Y.: Rensselaer Polytechnic Institute, 1954).

[7] *Chemical and Engineering News*, December 29, 1958, p. 77.

[8] B. D. Van Evera, "The College Chemistry Teacher," in *Careers in Chemistry and Chemical Engineering* (Washington, D.C.: American Chemical Society, 1950).

[9] *Chemical and Engineering News,* October 20, 1958, p. 94 (chart copyright 1958 by the American Chemical Society, and reprinted by permission).

[10] *Ibid.,* pp. 96–97.

[11] *Ibid.,* p. 96.

Chapter Three

[1] *New York Times,* January 29, 1959.

[2] *Chemical and Engineering News,* September 17, 1951, p. 3818.

[3] Dr. Linus Pauling, Preface to *Moments of Discovery,* edited by G. Schwartz and P. W. Bishop (New York: Basic Books, 1958).

[4] *New York Times,* November 23, 1958.

[5] "Climbing the Research Ladder," *Chemical and Engineering News,* December 3, 1956, p. 5920.

[6] *Chemical and Engineering News,* September 17, 1951, p. 3818.

[7] *Ibid.,* December 1, 1958, p. 72.

[8] John J. Carlin, "Do Courses in Chemistry and Physics at the High School Level Contribute to Success in Beginning College Chemistry?", *Journal of Chemical Education,* January, 1957.

[9] "Opportunities in Clinical Chemistry," *Chemical and Engineering News,* October 11, 1954.

[10] Personal communication to the author from an experienced chemist.

Chapter Four

[1] *Journal of Commerce,* November 25, 1958.

[2] *Allies in Defense—Some Facts About Synthetic Organic Chemicals* (New York: Organic Chemical Manufacturers Association, 1956), p. 27.

[3] "An Industrial Research Director Views Fundamental Research," *Chemical and Engineering News,* April 21, 1958, p. 85.

Chapter Five

[1] *Chemical and Engineering News,* June 23, 1958, p. 26.

[2] "Corrosion Fighters," *Science World,* February 24, 1959.

[3] Eugene G. Rochow, "Silicones," *New Chemistry* (New York: Simon and Schuster, Inc., 1957), p. 150.

[4] R. J. Thompson, Jr., "Rocket Propellants," *Chemical and Engineering News,* June 23, 1958, p. 67.

[5] Ronald S. Nyholm, "The Renaissance of Inorganic Chemistry," *Journal of Chemical Education,* April, 1957.

[6] *New Chemistry* (A Scientific American Book) (New York: Simon and Schuster, Inc., 1957), p. 3.

[7] *Ibid.*, p. 86.

CHAPTER SIX

[1] *Industrial and Engineering Chemistry* (Analysis Edition) (Washington, D.C.: American Chemical Society, 1930), II, 201.

[2] *Ibid.*, XIX, No. 11, p. 941.

[3] Beverly L. Clarke, "The Role of Analytical Chemistry in Industrial Research," *Journal of Chemical Education*, December, 1957.

[4] *Industrial and Engineering Chemistry*, XIX, No. 11, p. 941.

[5] *Chemical and Engineering News*, XXVII, December 26, 1949, p. 3866.

[6] Clarke, *op. cit.*, p. 1301.

CHAPTER SEVEN

[1] Joseph S. Fruton and Sophia Simmonds, *General Biochemistry*, Second Edition (New York: John Wiley & Sons, Inc., 1953), p. 1.

[2] *New York Times*, November 20, 1958.

[3] Edwin B. Kurtz, Jr., "Chemical Basis for Adaptation in Plants," *Science*, November 7, 1958, p. 1117.

[4] *New York Times*, February 19, 1959.

CHAPTER EIGHT

[1] H. D. Crockford and S. B. Knight, *Fundamentals of Physical Chemistry for Premedical Students* (New York: John Wiley & Sons, Inc., 1958).

[2] From an address by Dr. Libby before the Manufacturing Chemists' Association, Inc., November 25, 1958, in New York.

[3] *The Chemical Industry Facts Book*, Third Edition (Manufacturing Chemists' Association, 1957), p. 97.

[4] United States Atomic Energy Commission, *Uses of Isotopes in Industry and in Physical and Chemical Research* (n.d.), p. 47.

[5] Willard F. Libby, "Chemistry and the Peaceful Uses of the Atom," *Chemical and Engineering News*, May 6, 1957, p. 15.

[6] United States Department of Labor, Bureau of Labor Statistics, *Employment Outlook in the Atomic Energy Field*, 1957, p. 419.

[7] *Time*, November 17, 1958.

CHAPTER NINE

[1] Anthony Standen, "The First Seventy-five Years," *Chemical and Engineering News*, August 13, 1951, p. 3248.

[2] *Ibid.*

[3] Thomas K. Sherwood, "Graduate Training in Chemical Engineering," *Chemical and Engineering News,* August 7, 1950.

[4] Standen, *op. cit.*

[5] Sherwood, *op. cit.*

[6] "Chemical Apparatus in the United States," Report No. 23 of Technical Assistance Mission (Organization for European Economic Co-Operation, 1952), p. 36.

CHAPTER TEN

[1] *The Chemical Industry: A Symposium* (Troy, N.Y.: Rensselaer Polytechnic Institute, 1953), p. 35.

[2] *Journal of Commerce,* November 20, 1958.

CHAPTER ELEVEN

[1] Betty Lou Raskin, "Woman's Place Is in the Lab, Too," *New York Times Magazine,* April 19, 1959, p. 17.

[2] *Ibid.,* p. 19.

[3] *Chemical and Engineering News,* March 28, 1955.

[4] National Manpower Council, *Womanpower* (New York: Columbia University Press, 1957), p. 244.

[5] *Ibid.,* p. 240.

[6] United States Department of Labor, *Women's Bureau Bulletin* No. 264, 1958.

[7] *Chemical and Engineering News,* June 23, 1958.

[8] Eleanor M. Ullman, "Women in the Chemical Industry," *Industrial and Engineering Chemistry,* February, 1958.

[9] *New York Times,* January 20, 1959.

[10] Katherine Stinson, "Some Facts About Engineering as a Career for Women," in *Women in Engineering* (Society of Women Engineers, 1958).

[11] *Chemical and Engineering News,* September 17, 1951, p. 3847.

Index

A

ACTH, 84
adsorption, 98
agricultural chemist, 53, 89, 90, 91
agriculture and food chemistry, 19
alchemist, 4, 5, 6, 7, 55
alpha rays, 12
Allfrey, V. G., 82
amines, 83
American Chemical Society, 18, 108, 124, 126, 127, 129, 135
American Cyanamid Corp., 127
American Institute of Chemical Engineers, 132
antibiotics, 43, 79, 80, 113
analytical chemists, 68 *et seq.*
aptitude tests, 32
Aristotle, 6
Arrhenius, S., 31
atomic energy, 66, 101-104
Atomic Energy Commission, 25
atom, 10, 12
Ashbaugh, B., 60
aureomycin, 80
Autoanalyzer, 71, 72

B

Bacon, R., 6
Baeyer, A., 41
Barkdoll, A., 27
Becker, J. J., 7, 37
Bequerel, H., 11
Bell Aircraft Co., 64
Bernal, J. D., 106
Black, J., 8
biological chemistry, 19
Bohr, N., 12, 98
Bovet, D., 86
biochemistry, 9
biochemists, 19, 31, 42, 43, 77 *et seq.*
Boyle, R., 7, 69
Brandt, H., 55
Bullene, E. F., 17
Burkholder, P., 80

C

Calvin, M., 105
cancer, 80, 81
carbohydrates, 19

Carothers, W. H., 45
Carver, G. W., 52
cement chemistry, 63
Chain, E., 79
Chemical Abstracts, 18, 96
chemical engineering, 16, 47, 107-116
chemical industry, 14, 16, 17, 19, 22, 117, 133
chemical manufacturing, 15-17
chemical profession, 14, 15 *et seq.*, 133
chemical engineers, 64, 104, 107 *et seq.*, 130-132
chemist, definition of, 3, 4
chemurgy, 52, 53
chromatography, 70
Clarke, B. L., 76
clinical chemistry, 87, 88
college courses in chemistry, 35, 36
colleges for chemistry and chemical engineering, 134 *et seq.*
colloidal chemistry, 19
Condon, E. U., 30, 31
Conant, J. B., 15, 16, 133
commercial chemical development, 120 *et seq.*
Commercial Chemical Development Assn., 122, 123
consultant, 73
conservation of matter, 8
Corning Glass Works, 61-63
cortisone, 83, 84
corrosion, 59, 60, 74, 111
Cosulich, D., 127
Crawford, H. M., 127
Crucible Steel Co., 58
Curie, M. S., 11, 126
Curie, P., 11, 126

D

Dalton, J., 10
Dacron, 20, 46

Delrin, 27, 28
demand for chemists, 22, 23, 104, 113, 115
Democritus, 12
direct hydrogen reduction, 59
doctoral degree, 36, 37
Doering, W. E., 42
Dow Chemical Co., 30, 33, 58, 121
du Pont de Nemours & Company, E. I., 19, 20, 27, 28, 33, 45, 46, 120
Dow, H. H., 20
Dvorkovitz, V., 91

E

Eddy, N. B., 87
education for chemistry, 25, 34-36, 44, 122, 129, 135-38
electron, 12
elements, 5, 7, 8, 10
Eliot, C., 10
Empedocles, 5, 6

F

fermentation, 113, 114
fertilizer and soil chemistry, 19
Fischer, E., 78
Fleming, A., 79
Flemming, A. S., 87, 131, 132
Florey, H. W., 79
Froelich, C., 131
Food and Drug Administration, 74
food chemist, 91 *et seq.*

G

gas and fuel chemistry, 19
geochemist, 104-106
General Electric Co., 62
glass chemistry, 60-63
government chemists, 21, 22
Goodale, C. D., 122
Gray, H., 27

H

Haber process, 97
herbicides, 52
Hevesy, G. von, 27, 103
high school requirements for chemistry, 35
high temperature chemistry, 66
Hill, J., 45
Hochwalt, C. A., 29
Hoff, G. P., 46
Hoffman, K., 85
Horsey, E. T., 125
"hot atom" chemistry, 66
Hutchinson, M. H., 132
Hyde, J. F., 62
Hughes, H. D., 120

I

income of chemists, 23-25, 33, 36, 37, 53, 88, 104, 114, 115, 129, 130
infrared spectrometer, 21
industrial analytical chemist, 75
industrial research, 111, 112
inorganic chemist, 19, 37, 55 *et seq.*
inorganic compounds, 11
ion exchange, 66, 67
ionization, 31
insecticides, 4, 16

J

Jewett, F., 13
Johnson, L. E., 123
Jones and Loughlin Co., 59

K

Kekule, F., 13
Kendall, E. C., 83, 84

kinetics, 97
Kinzel, A. B., 125
Koch, T., 28
Krathwohl, W. C., 29
Kurtz, E. B., 89

L

Lagrange, J. L., 9
Langmuir, I., 98
Lavoisier, A. L., 8, 9, 29, 69, 78
Leopold, A. K., 128
Libby, W. F., 25, 104
Liebig, J., 13, 18

M

MacDonald, R., 28
Malamud, W., 86
Magnus, A., 6
mathematics, as a requirement for chemistry, 35, 96
May, E. L., 87
Mendeleev, D. I., 10, 11, 29
medicine and chemistry, 78, 81-82, 84-88
metal chemistry, 57-59
microchemistry, 76
Millikan, R., 12
Miner, H. I., 126
Mirsky, A. E., 82
Monsanto Chemical Co., 16, 29, 33, 56
missiles, 63, 64
Myatt, D. W. O., 33

N

National Manpower Council, 128
Nogare, S. D., 28
North American Aviation, Inc., 65
Noyes, W. A., 31
nylon, 45, 46

O

organic compound, 11, 13, 30
organic chemistry, 19, 53, 78
organic chemists, 19, 37, 38 *et seq.*
Orlon, 46

P

paint, plastics and printing ink chemistry, 19
Paracelsus, 6, 7, 78
Pasteur, L., 79
Pauling, L. C., 31, 80, 86
Patnode, W., 62
Perkin, W. H., 41
penicillin, 42, 43, 79
periodic table, 10
petrochemicals, 18, 47
petroleum chemistry, 46, 47
physical chemist, 35, 96 *et seq.*
phlogiston theory, 7, 9
plastics, 17, 28, 44, 45, 53, 56
polymers, 19, 27, 28, 44
Price, D., 125
Priestley, J., 9
product evaluation, 87
propellants, 63-65
proteins, 84
Punderson, J., 28
Preising, M. J., 127

Q

qualifications for chemistry, 26 *et seq.*

R

radiochemistry, 102, 103
radioisotopes, 90, 103
radium, 12
Raskin, B. L., 124
rayon, 46
reserpine, 85

research, 20, 22, 23, 27, 33, 43, 54, 75, 123, 125, 127, 129
Roentgen, W. K., 11
rockets, 56, 63, 64
Rutherford, E., 12, 98
Ryden, L., 30
rubber chemistry, 19

S

Sanger, F., 84, 85
salaries—see *income*
sales promotion, 123
Salernus, 6
Scalera, M., 54
Sheehan, J. C., 42
specialization in chemistry, 18, 19
spectroanalyzer, 72
Sloan, A. P., 81
spectroscopy, 98, 99
Schultz, J., 81
Shriner, R. L., 34
silicones, 62
stereochemistry, 13, 73
structural formula, 39
Stadnichenko, T., 127
Stahl, G. E., 7
synthesis of drugs, 41-43
synthetic fibers, 3, 4, 16, 20, 45, 53
synthetic rubber, 16, 17
Sylvius, F., 7, 8
synthetic elements, 66

T

technical salesman, 117 *et seq.*
teaching chemistry, 22, 23
terramycin, 29, 80
Telkes, M., 126
Teller, E., 102
Thales, 5
Theophilus, 6
thermodynamics, 97
Thompson, R. J., 65
Thomson, J. J., 12

U

ultramicrochemistry, 76
Union Carbide Company, 20, 60, 125

V

Van de Graaf accelerator, 71
vital force, 11
vocational guidance, 29, 131

W

Waksman, S. A., 80
Warnock, M. D., 34
water, sewerage and sanitation chemistry, 19
Whister, R. L., 53
Whistler, J. M., 32
Wohler, F., 11, 13, 39, 69
woman chemists, 124 *et seq.*
Woodward, R. B., 42
Wrinch, D., 127